DESIGNING POWER & SAIL

ARTHUR EDMUNDS

Executive Editor: Robert "Bob" Lollo
Editor: John P. Kaufman
Copy Editor: Phyllis Klucinec

BRISTOL FASHION PUBLICATIONS
Enola, Pennsylvania

Published by Bristol Fashion Publications

ISBN: 1-892216-05-1

Library of Congress Catalog Card Number: 98-071301

Contribution acknowledgments

Cover Design: Design by John P. Kaufman. Line Graphics by Arthur Edmunds.
Inside Graphics/Photos: by Arthur Edmunds unless otherwise indicated.

INTRODUCTION

Fortunately, I have been able to work with boat owners, crew, boatyards, manufacturers and custom builders, over a thirty year period. All of these endeavors have been a rewarding experience. We have learned from each other and from the problems that have occurred. These problems bring out questions from everyone and surprisingly, the same questions are not heard twice.

This book will answer the design questions everyone has asked. It will prove valuable to boat owners and all those interested in the marine business. The chapters are organized in the same order a designer uses to approach the problems of a new design. Each phase of the design process is explained in minute detail so that every reader can see the procedure designers use to achieve a successful boat.

New material included in this book has not been previously published and will prove to be valuable to practicing designers and to all the boating public. Speed predictions can be made from the new formula for fast hulls. In addition, a new formula has been developed for the design pressure on hull bottoms. These are used with speeds to 50 knots (93 km/hr and hull lengths to 120 feet (37 m). I have developed both formulas after years of research and testing.

Very few designers enjoy the luxury of designing one type of boat: sail or power; commercial fisherman or sport fisherman; fast motor yacht or trawler yacht. Most designers must draw any type of hull in any material to be used in any operating area. There isn't any narrow area of design that applies only to sailboats, fishing boats or passenger ferries. Throughout this book, the principles of hull design are noted to apply to all types of vessels, both work boats and pleasure craft, in the same range of relative speed. It is only above the waterline where the apparent differences are noticed.

Formulas and mathematical relationships are given so people interested in drawing a new design will have all the necessary data. The mathematics are not complicated and an inexpensive scientific calculator can be used as this will show powers and roots of numbers. When reading the book for the first time, I do suggest reading only the text without attempting to understand the formulas. Subsequent readings and reference use may then incorporated the formulas. Following this advice will help you completely understand the entire design process without over involvement in the mathematics.

As my experiences increase, I am continually amazed at the inventiveness of many designers and builders. I can't walk through a boat yard or a boat show without discovering a new technique, however small in the total concept of the hull. Many of these ideas are eventually printed in the boating magazines, greatly contributing to the improvement of the boating industry. I am deeply appreciative of these efforts and thank the many people who work towards better boats.

Arthur Edmunds

TABLE OF CONTENTS

Level trim - Reference dimensions - Weight groups - List of items to be totaled - Areas of curved surfaces - Simpson's Rule - Pounds per inch immersion of the hull.

Hull weight comparison - Criteria for a hull material - Hull design bottom pressure Hull bottom thickness - Size of framing - Weight comparison of framing - Aluminum, steel and plastic composites properties - Examples of calculations for glass fiber, wood, ferro-cement - Deck loads - Laminates with a core.

Type of flotation and placement - Calculation for the required amount of foam - Densities of materials.

The speed/length ratio - Determining boat speed - Reduction gears - Minimum propeller diameter - Propeller diameter and pitch - Propeller location and rotation - Number of blades - The propeller shaft and bearings.

Important design factors - The chine line - Deadrise angle - Prismatic coefficient - Preliminary lines - Displacement calculations - Planing powerboat hull lines - Moderate speed powerboat hull lines - Displacement speed powerboat hull lines - Sailboat hull lines - Catamarans - Table of offsets.

Forces that right the boat - Calculating the righting arm - Evaluating stability - The Rahola criterion - Multihull stability, power and sail - Hull flooding.

CHAPTER ONE

THE CLIENT & THE DESIGNER

The boat owner who hires a designer expects to know at their first meeting what the designer will provide and exactly what the designer will need to know from the owner. This chapter will present those requirements, which will prove invaluable to both parties in conducting business on mutually acceptable terms.

If you ask for a sportfisherman, motorsailer, passenger ferry or catamaran, a good designer should be prepared to give you exactly what you want. Some designers seem to specialize in one type of boat only because they have long experience with that hull design. A specialized business attracts more of the same. Often, a designer who usually works with tug boats may be found racing sailboats on the weekend. It is a mistake to compartmentalize an individual's talents.

The client should give the designer as much detail as possible to convey his exact requirements for the use of the boat. The designer must agree or explain why a certain feature may not be appropriate. The designer's job is to prepare drawings for use by the builder to communicate the owner's specifications and exactly how to accomplish them.

Often, the boat is built on another continent from the designer's office. Each drawing should be sufficiently accurate to avoid constant questions from builder to designer to owner. Each drawing should have the material used, how to put it together, fastenings and the surface finish for each part. Especially important is the mention of equipment to be purchased by the owner and installed by the builder.

THE DRAWINGS AND FEES

After preliminary discussions concerning the nature of the vessel, the owner will naturally want to know what the designer will charge for the drawings. The complexity of any design will greatly affect the engineering time required. Usually, a thirty foot (9.2 m) hull will require 200 hours; a 50 foot (15.3 m) boat uses 500 hours; and over 1200 hours will be required for a 90 foot (27.4 m) hull. The designer will charge his time at an hourly rate which is approximately the same as the local boat yards.

The following is a list of drawings for any design but the list could be twice as long if the boat is complex and has a large amount of equipment. The number of drawings also varies widely with each project and is dependent on how much information the builder requires. On a large vessel it is often necessary to have a detail drawing for each bulkhead and partition. These drawings will show the framing, attachment of joinerwork and the penetration of plumbing and electrical wiring. Separate electrical drawings for each AC (110v & 220v) and DC (12v, 24v & 32v) voltages are sometimes required.

Outboard Profile	Construction Plan
Arrangement Plan	Construction Profile
Calculation of Weights	Deck Plan
Hull Lines	Sail Plan & Ballast
Table of Offsets	Engineroom Plan
Sections	Stability Calculations

A SHORT HISTORY OF BOAT DRAWINGS

In boat building history, scaled construction drawings were not made until the early part of the nineteenth century. Previously, a boat builder was trained to construct one type of boat indigenous to his part of the world. Everyone relied on his skill and adaptability rather than plans. Whether rowed or sailed, the same hull was used for cargo, fishing or exploration.

As the need for longer and wider boats evolved, the builders made wood models of their projects to instruct their workers and for the approval of the owners. The shape of the model was based solely on one man's experience, intelligence and the limitations of his ability to bend wood planks.

The industry advanced rapidly in the seventeenth and eighteenth centuries, as improvements based on trial and error were constantly applied to succeeding hulls. Wood models were then delineated with inked waterlines (horizontal planes parallel to the desired (designed) waterline) and sections (vertical planes perpendicular to the waterlines) and sometimes a drawing was made on paper. Dimensions on the model were then transferred to the mold loft floor to make full size patterns.

As drawings were made of every hull model, the differences became more apparent. When one completed boat proved much faster, the drawings were carefully studied to find out why. The need for more accurate, scaled drawings became obvious in the period before accurate instrumentation for either boats or models. As hull engineering became more advanced and the marine industry more diversified, detailed drawings were demanded for every phase of boat construction.

SCALES AND MEASUREMENT

Each drawing is made to a certain scale, depending on the amount of detail to be shown and the size of the part, assembly or hull. The hull lines are normally drawn to one of the following scales:

Boats under 30 ft. (9.2 m)	1" = 1' 0" (1:12)	1:10 metric
Boats 30 - 65 ft. (9.2 m -19.8 m)	3/4" = 1' 0" (1:16)	1:20 metric
Boats over 65 ft. (19.8 m)	1/2" = 1' 0" (1:24)	1:25 metric

It is easy to see why fractions and inches are clumsy and why tenths of a foot are more practical. Land surveyors have been using the latter system for years. Great Britain was wise to change their money to the decimal system and other countries would be wise to change their system of measurement.

The metric system International Standard (SI), is used throughout the world and this book uses the following equivalents in measurement:

1 inch = 25.4 mm	1 lb = .4536 kg (kilogram)
1 foot = .3048 meter	1 kg = 9.81 Newton (N)
1 sqft = .0929 sqm	1 lb = 4.448 Newton (N)

1 inch^3 = 16.4 cm^3

1 inch^4 = 416,231 mm^4

1 knot = 1.854 km/hr

1 in - lb = .113 N-m

Sea Water is 64 lb/ft^3 (1025 kg/m^3).

1 Pascal (Pa) = 1 N/m^2

1 psi = 6.895 kPa (kilopascal)

Accell. gravity = 9.8 m/sec^2

=32.2 ft/sec^2

If you are not familiar with the new SI system, there is some terminology that should be clarified. The English system uses pounds to measure weight (mass), force or pressure. In the SI system, weight is in kilograms (kg), force is in Newtons (N) and pressure (stress) is in Pascals (Pa).

Some adults and most young people have looked at the car speedometer and have found that 25 mph is 40 km/hr; 50 mph is 80 km/hr; and 55 mph is 88 km/hr. The key ratio is one kilometer is about 5/8 of a statute (land) mile. But when discussing boat speed or navigation, a nautical mile of 6080 feet (1854 m) is used, not the 5280 feet (1610 m) of a land mile.

CURVED HULL LINES AND OTHER DRAWINGS

Most boat owners have asked me how the long curved lines of the hull and other drawings are accomplished. In the sections or other detail drawings, the short, curved lines are drawn with Copenhagen Ships Curves, which have been cut from a sheet of flat plastic. When drawing the lines of the hull, the use of a spline and weights is essential (Figure 1-1). The spline is a piece of wood or plastic about 1/4" (6 mm) by 1/8" (3 mm) in section and 72 inches (1830 mm) in length. It is held in place with 3 lb (1.3 kg) lead weights that have a hook on one end This spline is used to draw the continuous fair curves of the hull without discontinuities. Fifteen to twenty weights are used to hold the spline in place.

A smooth, fair curve of the hull line is formed by placing the weights on a spline in a curve that you estimate to be correct. Each weight is then lifted off the paper, one at a time and the spline is carefully observed to detect any movement. Movement indicates the line is not a fair curve. The weight is then replaced on the spline and the adjacent weight is lifted. This process is repeated until the lifting of each weight separately, does not result in <u>any</u> movement of the spline. Drawing a fair line takes time and patience and it is the essence of the art of hull design. Some wag once said old boat designers never die; they just get a little dinghy! I'm sure the condition results from using a spline and weights.

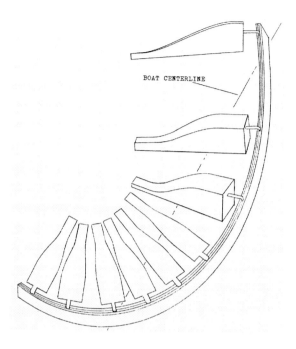

BOAT CENTERLINE

Figure 1-1

Spline and Spline Weights

Drawing a sailboat waterline. The weights hold the spline in a fair line and are always placed on the inside of the curve. A lead or pen scribes the line on the outside of the curve.

There are computer programs available for the production of hull lines in a smooth, fair curve but the input of data must be checked to ensure the desired curve is generated. The dimensions of the principal lines (sheer, hull at centerline and chine or waterline) must be entered into the program after they are taken from the original lines drawn on paper. In fact, it is not unusual for the complete set of computer generated curves to require as much time as the manual drawing. But, the computer is most valuable in producing changes to the hull lines after the initial set has been generated. When large drawings are required, an expensive plotter (type of printer) is required to reproduce the images on paper.

Large corporations use computer drawings to interface with plasma-arc plate cutting equipment and with automated routers to shape joinerwork. These techniques are especially important for a manufacturer building a large number of identical boats. When making cavity molds for glass fiber boats, a male plug (pattern) must first be made. These wood or plastic foam male plugs can now be made on a computer controlled milling machine, to very close tolerances. *Chapter Eighteen* discusses computer design.

SUMMARY

This chapter has described some of the initial questions a boat owner has when first meeting with a designer. Succeeding chapters will show the complete design process in the same sequence the designer uses to sort the many details into a complete set of drawings.

CHAPTER TWO

STYLING

The first drawing an owner wants to see is the exterior view (outboard profile) of his boat so he can be assured the final product will be unique and outstanding. This outboard profile, also called the styling drawing, shows exactly how the boat appears sitting in the water, above the waterline. It is the creative art in boat design, as the other drawings primarily show engineering competence. An entire design is sold by the designer on the basis of this one drawing and it forms the showcase in the portfolio that is used to obtain future business. In this chapter we'll examine five key challenges to creating a successful styling drawing for any type of boat.

BEAUTY AND THE ENGINEERING BEAST

A good styling drawing is the best advertising any designer can have. Almost everyone will judge a designer on this one exterior profile, rather than other drawings showing engineering talent. Most designers who have an engineering background have little artistic flair. They often give a rough sketch, to scale, to an industrial designer who is hired to develop a beautiful styling profile. If an unusual boat is planned, the views from the bow and stern are sometimes requested.

Just as beauty is in the eye of the observer, an owner may want a boat that looks like many others or they may insist on an unconventional form to be distinctive among their peers. In actual practice, the hull and superstructure shape above the waterline can be most anything the owner desires. Within good safety practices, it is generally accurate to say the shape of the boat above the waterline is primarily based on artistic development and the operational requirements. The shape of the hull below the waterline is derived from engineering calculations based on weight, shape, trim and speed. The thinking of the designer is separated into two areas, above and below the waterline.

Styling excellence is accomplished by drawing many sketches until the proportions are the best the designer can achieve. The sketches may be changed many times before deciding on the best profile. The height of the deck house (superstructure) is determined by the inside headroom required. The height of the hull (freeboard) at the sheer (intersection of the deck and the hull) has to be adjusted to obtain the most pleasing relationship between the hull and the deck house. A sailboat usually has a very small trunk cabin or projection above the deck as all the interior accommodations are in the hull and the hull height dominates. If there are two or three decks in a powerboat, the height of the hull (freeboard) is increased to reveal a good appearance. At times, the sheer may be much higher than the main deck. Too high or too low an amount of freeboard can be unattractive.

Certainly, the exterior styling must fit the arrangement of the interior and particular attention is given to bulkheads, windows and ladders. This shows the interdependence of one drawing on another. The height and length of the interior requirements must be drawn at the same time as the exterior styling and each drawing changed so they all agree.

The line of the interior decks may not necessarily show on the exterior as the shapes of the sides of the superstructure (cabin side) are independent and continuous in structure. The edge of the roof or bridge, may be curved to the shape of the sheer or other smooth line. The line of the bottom of the windows may curve to fit the styling and it does not have to be parallel to the interior floor. Just a glance at the boating magazines will quickly reveal what is good styling and what is not acceptable. Good ideas often develop from both the good work and mistakes of others but copying is a shabby practice.

EXAMPLES OF STYLING

The hulls shown on Figures 2-1 through 2-8 have some of the possible combinations of bow shape, stern shape and curvature of sheer for both powerboats and sailboats. All the sketches can be used on successful boats but the hull and superstructure shapes must be compatible with each other. Certainly, these example sketches can be improved in many ways and special purpose boats usually require unique styling.

The shape of the hull sides and stern is a matter of individual taste but one comment can be made about the stern that slopes forward from the aftermost point to the deck. When this form is used in a small hull, the deck length is shorter by the amount of slope in the transom. This might be an important point in a boat less than 30 feet (9.2 m) where we want the cockpit length to be as long as possible. This forward slope of the transom was first used in racing sailboats in an attempt to reduce pitching in sloppy seas. The reduced weight of the stern structure lessens the tendency for pitching. In racing, creature comforts are considered secondary to speed.

REQUIRED HEADROOM

One of the most troublesome parts of good styling is seven feet (2.1m) of headroom is required for every level of the boat. 6'6" (2 m) + headliner + roof beams + roof thickness. Each profile drawing must reflect this headroom and show the exact height of the sheer and cabin top (roof). Experience has shown the interior floor (cabin sole) cannot be lower than the designed waterline in a boat, under 60 feet (18.3 m) and usually not more than a foot (0.3 m) below the waterline in larger hulls. Since the top of the roof must be seven feet (2.1 m) above the waterline in a boat with accommodations in the hull, we have a reference height to start the styling drawing. If the deck house is over the engineroom, about eleven feet (3.355 m) is required between the roof and the waterline.

These dimensions apply to a 30 foot (9.2 m) or a 60 foot (18.3 m) hull and the smaller boat will have a proportionately higher sheer line to achieve a pleasing balance between the height of the hull and the height of the deck house. In reality, the shorter hull is more difficult to style in an acceptable manner. When the best styling is required in a boat under 30 feet (9.2 m), there is often less than standing headroom if the design does not include a deck house.

HULL BEAM

While the heights of each deck are constant in different length hulls, the beam varies widely, according to the interior equipment requirements and the necessity for increased stability. Before World War II, boats were rather narrow as it was correctly thought a slimmer hull has less resistance, as in a canoe. Also, there was less demand for large galleys, lounges and navigation desks.

Larger engines and auxiliary mechanical equipment have become in demand on recreational yachts and the hull beam has been increased. Modern boats generally have a ratio of waterline length to waterline beam of 4:1 in lengths less than 60 feet (18.3 m). One hundred foot (30.5 m) hulls have a ratio about 5:1 and aircraft carriers have a ratio about 10:1. Above the waterline, the beam may curve inboard (tumblehome) or flare outboard. The latter is illustrated in Figure 2-7 which provides for a side deck outboard of a wider deck house or trunk cabin.

For many years, it was considered good styling to have the hull sides of sailboats curve inboard in the middle of the hull (tumblehome). When glass fiber boats became numerous, this tumblehome was dropped as the hull could not be released from the one piece mold some manufacturers desired. Thus, sailboat hull sides became almost vertical. I designed a sailboat hull with the sides flaring out slightly. This was rejected by the client as being too unconventional. A few years later, many cruising sailboats as well as the America's Cup boats all had flare to the hull sides. The resulting wider deck allows the crew to sit further outboard, effectively placing them in the "hiked out" position. Temporary fads are sometimes perceived as good styling.

EXTERIOR HARDWARE

It is important to show every detail of the deck fittings on the styling drawing and later in the deck plan, exactly as the boat will be seen when completed. If each item is carefully drawn to scale, the overall appearance of the drawing is improved and there will be less chance of access problems and interference with the proper operation of the boat. It is often difficult to draw a small part such as a 3 inch (7.6 cm) high cleat or chock when you are working to a scale of ¼ inch to the foot (1:48). It is better to have a single line denote a cleat or a hatch cover, as anything more would stand out on the drawing to a greater degree than it will on the full size hull.

The same reasoning applies to handrails and lifelines. If drawn with a double line, they stand out like a fence and detract from the superstructure. Some designers leave the handrails out of the styling profile. Important gear such as life rafts, tenders, deck lockers and antennae must appear exactly as they will be installed.

WINDOWS AND PORTLIGHTS

Nothing detracts from the appearance of the hull like poorly drawn windows. Their line and shape must be consistent with exterior styling and their number and size do not have to be the same on both sides of the boat. If possible, the bottom of each window should not be higher than 39 inches (1.0 m) for good visibility when seated and the top does not have to be higher than 72 inches (1.8 m) above the interior floor. Powerboat windshields in front of the helm may be higher.

As many windows as possible should open for good ventilation and they must have screens. There should not be any opening windows in the hull side for reasons of safety. The engineroom air intake should be above the sheer (intersection of deck and hull).

When you look at a boat in a photo or from a distance, the windows appear black as the interior is not brightly lit. Some designers have carried this to the styling drawing, showing a long, black stripe in place of the window detail. Sailboats usually have ports in the cabin side which are not level but parallel to the sheer. There is no reason for ports or windows to be parallel to the waterline or to the interior floor. All windows should have a twenty degree slope to the bottom frame so that water will drain away from the glass, even when the cabin side is raked inboard.

Many custom boats, of any material, have the window glass set inside the cabin side opening with bedding compound and an interior frame. An exterior trim ring or frame, is used outside the glass to keep it watertight. All window glass should be safety plate. Manufacturers of marine windows will usually produce custom shapes to the builder's specifications, including windshields and curved corner windows. Costs can be reduced by using the manufacturers standard marine window sizes.

MULTIHULLS

There is no reason the profile of a multihull should be any less pleasing than that of a monohull. A trimaran has its equipment in the center hull with the addition of floats and a connecting structure (wing). The outboard floats may sometimes be used for storage or accommodations and the overall styling may be of a powerboat or sailboat. A catamaran's two hulls pose the same challenge as a monohull. There must be standing headroom if berths and heads are installed. This sometimes makes the hull appear too high but a lower, more appealing, sheer line can be used with a headroom box (exterior seat) as shown on Figure 2-7. *Chapter Nine,* explains the reasons for a minimum height of the connecting structure above the water. It is poor practice to lower the deck house on centerline to achieve a lower profile for reasons of styling.

SUMMARY

The problems of good styling are a low profile, a good balance between the heights of the hull and superstructure and windows that are pleasing with the longitudinal lines of the sheer and the deck house. Each design presents a new challenge that can be met by drawing many rough sketches until the best appearance is found. Good styling must always fit in with the practical operations of the boat.

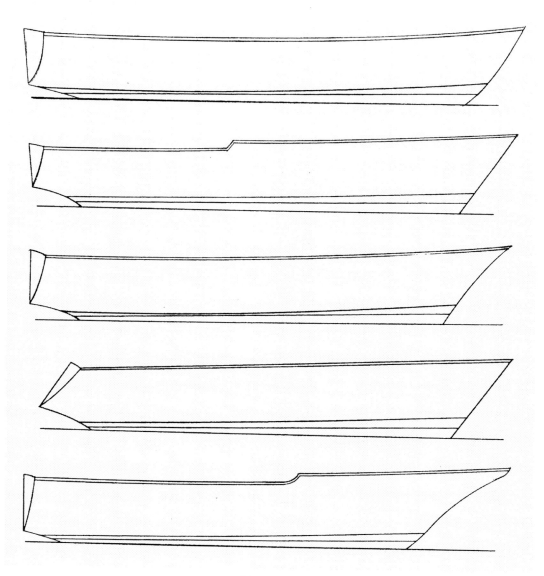

Figure 2-1

A few variations of sailboat hulls

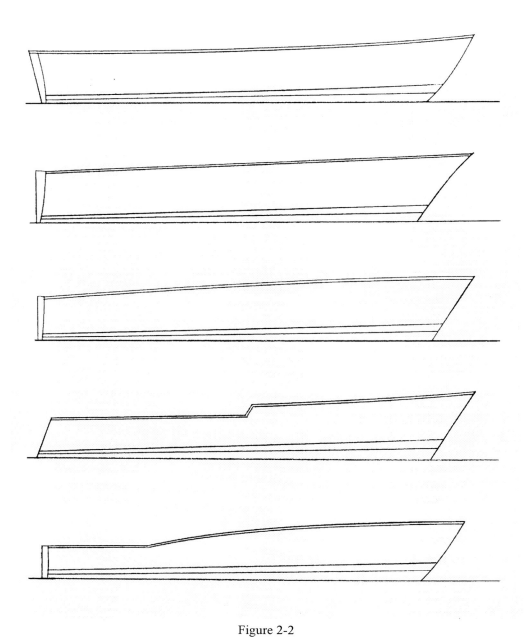

Figure 2-2

There are many variations of sheer lines and stem shapes for powerboat hulls.

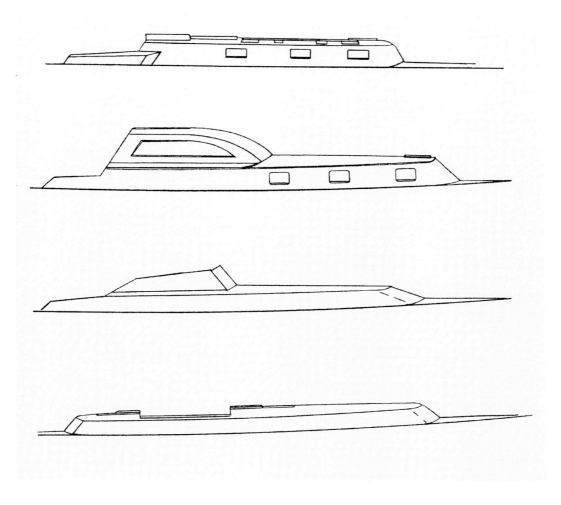

Figure 2-3

A few sailboat profiles, above the hull.

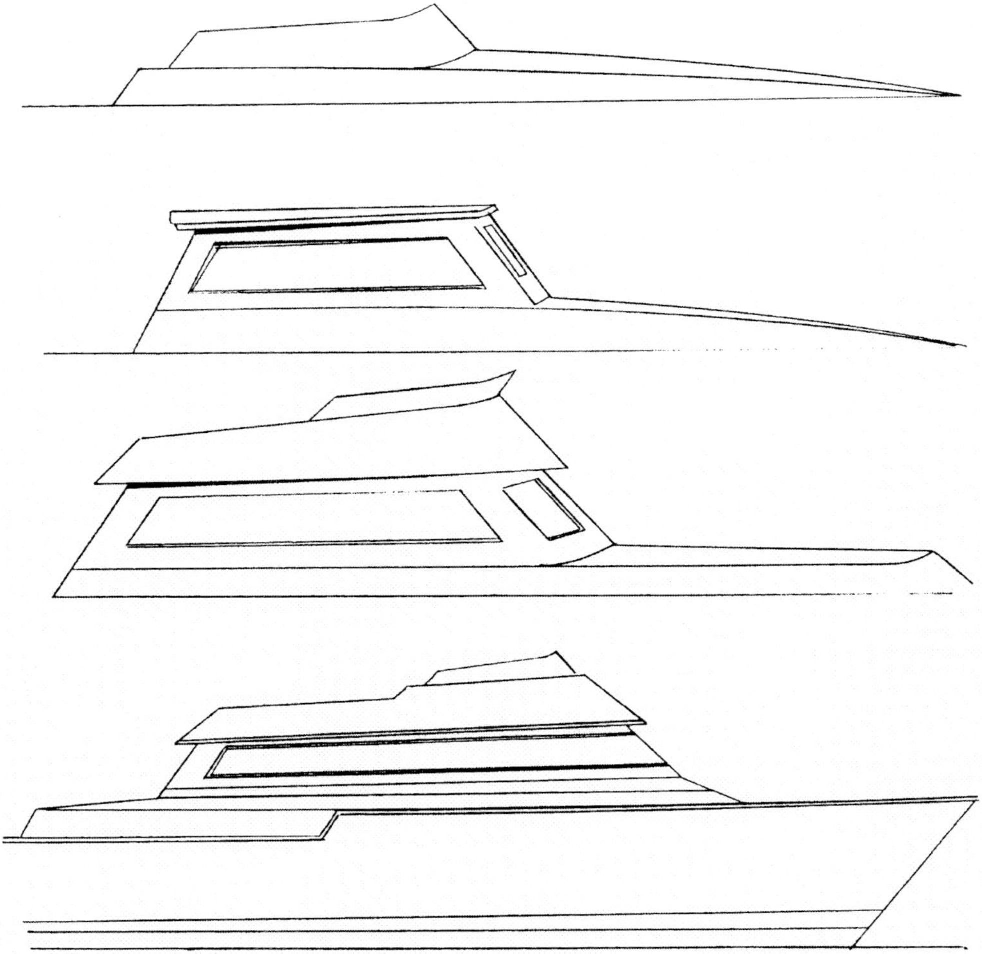

Figure 2-4

A few powerboat deck house profiles.

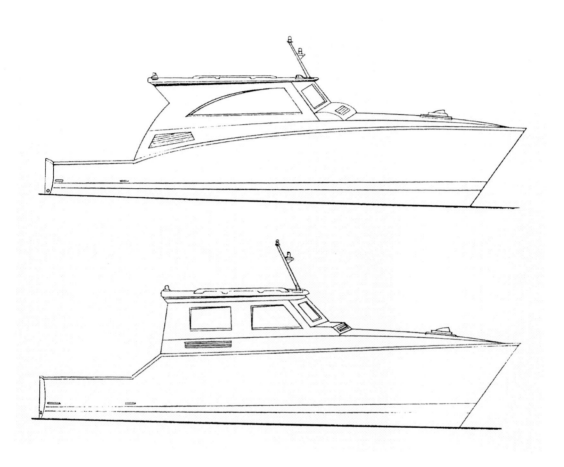

Figure 2-5

Two impressions of a thirty foot powerboat. Most people prefer an enclosed steering station to protect them from the elements. Below the windshield is a water trap vent box which provides air to the interior.

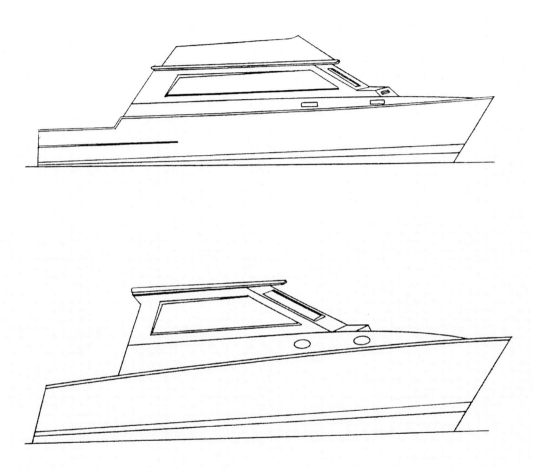

Figure 2-6

Profiles of a 56 foot and a 29 foot catamaran.

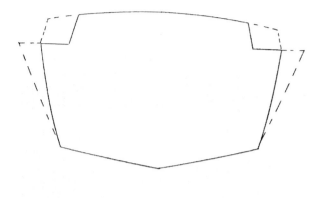

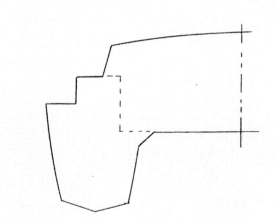

Figure 2-7

Upper: A section of a powerboat shows how flare of the hullside produces a wider beam at the deck and more room below decks. The beam at the waterline is not changed.

Lower: A partial section of a catamaran showing a headroom box over the hull. This gains headroom while maintaining a low sheer line.

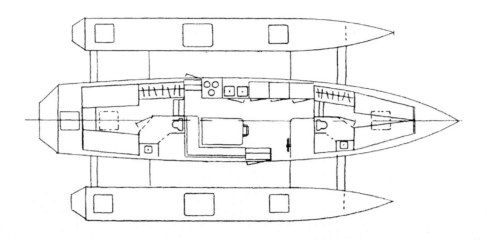

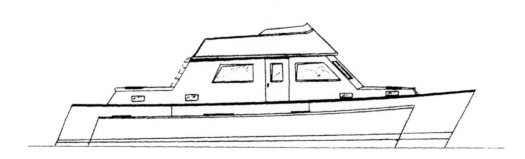

Figure 2-8

A 48 foot power trimaran with the engines and generator in the outboard hulls. This placement reduces noise and vibration in the cabin areas.

CHAPTER THREE

INTERIOR ARRANGEMENT PLAN

A major part of the owner's discussion with the designer will concern exactly what is required inside the hull. This chapter details the specific measurements used in building the interior cabinetry (joinerwork), which apply to all lengths of boats. This data should prove valuable to you who are planning an interior even though you usually have an arrangement in mind. Most owners have seen an interior plan they like in other boats. The boating magazines have many advertisements showing plans and photos.

THE INTERIOR OVERVIEW

The interior plan must be carefully drawn to scale, always remembering a person is about six feet (1.8 m) tall and 21 inches (.53 m) wide at the shoulders. In boats less than forty feet (12.2 m) in length, it is usual practice to have a 24 inch (.61 m) wide passageway near the boat's centerline as berths and a galley will consume all the available space on either side. The beam at a berth or counter height is normally two feet (.61 m) less than the maximum hull beam at any particular point. The cabin sole (floor) width tapers with the forward portion of the waterlines. It is often necessary to raise the floor forward to have sufficient width to walk to the forward berths.

All boats have berths, a head and a galley, even though the latter may be just a one burner stove. Larger hulls amplify on the bare necessities and have increased lounge space and the privacy of staterooms. As in any living area, storage space is always at a premium but vital for anything but day cruising. Today, owners are increasingly calling for an A.C. generator, washer, clothes dryer, a microwave oven, linen closets and a workbench.

The interior of a boat under 60 feet (18.3 m) is usually a series of compromises in attempting to fit all the comforts of home into a curved shape which has a fraction of the area. People who are not used to looking at boats say the interior looks small and cramped, which is just what they would say in comparing a small house to a large house. In a boat or a small house, not only are the rooms smaller but the floor area around the accommodations is minimal.

A powerboat may not have more interior living area than a sailboat of the same length but the powerboat does have more interior volume of air space. This is because the beam is wider, the freeboard higher and sometimes there is a deck house above the main deck. The powerboat may increase the interior volume even more by using a pronounced flare to the hull sides. This forms an exterior side deck that is wider than normal, allowing a wider cabin side. Figure 2-7.

The interior arrangement should be drawn in plan (top view) and section (end view) at the same time. This ensures the cabinetwork will not be reduced by the curvature of the hull and there is sufficient floor space. The cabin sole (floor) line must be drawn with reference to the sections so the owner can visualize the completed boat.

CHART DESK

The increasing use of electronic charts as well as paper charts, together with the latest multi-tasking, electronic marvels, brings the demand for a separate area dedicated to titillating transistors. A small boat may not have room for a chart desk and the galley counter is often used for this purpose. In addition to the electronics, there has to be storage for the radiotelephone (VHF), direction finder, fathometer, air horn, flashlights, GPS, emergency flares and the emergency radiobeacon (EPIRB).

Many drawers and lockers, plainly labeled, are always appreciated. The chart desk should be a minimum of 24 inches (0.6 m) by 36 inches (0.9 m). If there is not room for a seat, the end of a berth may be used. A wide drawer for flat storage of charts and navigating tools is very desirable and a red night light is a must.

THE GALLEY

The refrigerator or icebox, may be located where convenient in a sailboat but the range has to be gimbaled to swing athwartships so the pots remain level when the boat is heeled. If propane gas is used, the bottles must be stowed on deck with a shut off valve on deck and at the range. A gas detector must be located in the bilge. Propane and butane gas are heavier than air and may collect in the bilge if there is a leak. A spark or match will ignite any gas trapped anywhere in the boat. Compressed Natural Gas (CNG) is lighter than air but it still must be stored on deck. Good ventilation must be provided with all hatches closed, not only for comfort but it is a necessity when any open flame appliance is used anywhere in the hull.

It is always convenient to have a double sink in any boat, whatever the size. The galley sink in a sail-boat or small powerboat should be close to the centerline so it is above the waterline when the boat is heeled. If it is not above the waterline, the sink will not drain and sea water may enter. There is usually not a problem with the galley in a large powerboat as it may be located to fit with the other accommodations. Normal household appliances can be used in a larger boat as an A.C. generator is usually installed.

BERTHS

Sailboat berths should have the long dimension fore-and-aft as it is very uncomfortable to sleep with your head lower than your feet when the boat is heeled. On a powerboat with medium speed, the rolling is not as pronounced and berths can be athwartships when necessary. Some new designs are shown with a double bed that tapers at the foot, which allows more walking room around the bed. I can't imagine sleeping with this decreased foot room. It is much easier to use a rectangular mattress size that is readily available, even though a standard box spring cannot be used. It is usually not possible to carry a semi-rigid box spring into a boat, down a ladder and through a narrow stateroom door. The lack of a box spring can be eased somewhat by using tight, nylon webbing under the mattress instead of plywood. Single berths may have to be tapered in a sailboat but this can be tolerated when not in danger of kicking the spouse.

Single berths in the bow of a sailboat or powerboat are always uncomfortable as the forward 24 inches (0.6 m) is shared by both sleepers. One solution is to have one berth 24 inches (0.6 m) ahead of the other on the same level or the berths can be staggered in height. The forward ends can be overlapping with the lower berth 12 inches (0.3 m) above the floor and the upper berth 32 inches (0.8 m) above the floor. A single berth should be 27 inches (0.7 m) wide and 78 inches (2.0 m) in length.

If upper and lower berths are used on the same side of the hull, there should be a minimum of 81 inches (2.1m) of headroom in that stateroom. The berths and framing use 12 inches (0.3 m) of height and 28 inches (0.7 m) above the mattress is required for a person to enter the berth and turn over. Some racing sailboats have berths of very small size and thickness but this is only usable for a short period of time under Spartan living conditions.

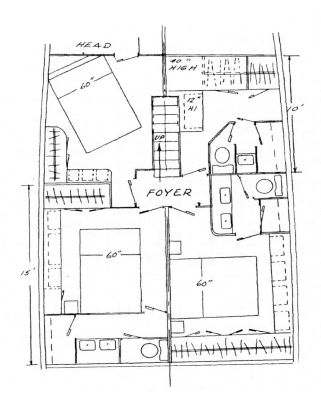

Figure 3-1

Four arrangements in a large powerboat.

Whenever possible, there should be drawers and lockers under the berths for each person. Reading lights and shelves outboard of each berth are a great convenience. It is more expensive to build a round corner in the joinerwork of a berth or counter but it is a sign of good design and craftsmanship. You will appreciate not bumping into a sharp corner.

It is sometimes efficient to have single berths at different heights and overlapping at right angles as shown in Figure 3-1. There must be at least 20 inches (0.5 m) of space above the foot of the lower berth. The open area under the upper berth may be used for a closet.

HEADS

Heads should be installed to comply with all governmental regulations, with either a self-contained or separate holding tank. A vented loop must be in the discharge line well above the waterline to prevent siphoning. The toilet space must be 24 inches (0.6 m) wide for comfortable seating.

Doors to the head often interfere with doors to the staterooms and there is a great tendency to use sliding (pocket) doors. But, the motion of the boat usually causes a sliding door to rattle, keeping everyone awake. One solution is to have the door slide at the bottom in an aluminum channel. Plastic strips on both sides ensure a close fit to prevent rattles. A door sill three inches (7.6c m) above the floor is very objectionable in a house but it is accepted on a boat. The conventional track and wheels at the top may be used or wheels may be used at the bottom edge.

The minimum width for a sink is 24 inches (0.6 m) and towel bars should be installed on each partition wall. It is very desirable to have a small drawer for toilet articles for each person on board plus space for clean towels and first-aid items. Figure 3-2 shows some typical head arrangements.

Shower areas can be as small as 24 inches (0.6 m) by 28 inches (0.7 m) in a sailboat but 30 inches (0.76 m) by 36 inches (0.9 m) is more desirable. The floor will have a plastic or aluminum pan with a pump to remove the shower water. Alternately, the pan can drain to a holding tank in the bilge. An air vent with water trap should be installed in the roof above the shower.

Since the shower area must be watertight and washable, glass fiber, aluminum or a plastic laminate (Formica, Micarta, Melamine, Consoweld and Corian are some trademarks) must be used for the side walls. In a small boat, the shower may be directly in front of the sink and toilet in the only standing area. In this case, a wood grating is used in the shower pan and a plastic curtain keeps the water contained in a small area.

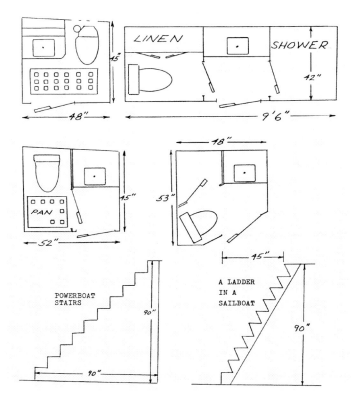

Figure 3-2

Head and stairs arrangements.

CUSTOMARY DIMENSIONS

Figure 3-3 lists dimensions that are always used in planning an interior. These are based on common uses in a house or on a boat and reflect what a person needs for comfortable living. The sizes of berths and appliances may be smaller in a boat, depending on the length of the boat and the owner's requirements. The dimensions are not restrictive and you may have new ideas which may be more comfortable or efficient.

MEASUREMENTS FOR INTERIOR FURNISHINGS		
Dimensions for reference	Inches	Meters
Shoulder room in a companionway, head or dining table	24	0.6
Counter height for standing comfort	36	0.9
Table height	29	0.74
Chair height	18	0.46
Head	18 x 21	.46 x .53
Locker depth	25	0.63
Locker rod height	63	1.6
Single bunk	30 or 36 x 78	.76 or .9 x 2.0
Double bunk	54 or 60 x 78	1.4 or 1.5 x 2.0
Household Appliances (Wide x Deep)		
Gimbaled boat stove	24	0.6
Refrigerator	33 x 29	.84 x .74
Range	30 x 24	.76 x .6
Double sink	33 x 24	.84 x .6
Dishwasher	24 x 24	.6 x .6
Washer or dryer	30 x 26	.74 x .66

Figure 3-3

The above dimensions are approximate and will vary with the manufacturer. Always refer to the catalogs. Commercial restaurant appliances will be larger and are sometimes used in large boats. Some galley fixtures used by the motor home industry are smaller.

Galley equipment and engines have to be replaced at some point. Therefore access must be provided. It is very embarrassing to have a 33 inch (0.84 m) wide refrigerator which was installed before the deck and a 30" (0.76 m) door to the deck house. Engines are removed through deck and roof hatches.

SUMMARY

This chapter has shown how important it is to have the arrangement plan drawn to an exacting scale. There are an infinite number of interior arrangements that may be planned, limited only by the imagination of the owner and the designer.

CHAPTER FOUR

SPECIFICATIONS FOR CONSTRUCTION AND DISSIMILAR METALS

The owner's input into the design process is expressed most clearly by the specifications for construction. This chapter lists what information the owner must provide for any type of boat, commonly called the specifications. An integral part of these specifications is the use of materials that are compatible with each other, particularly metals. A list and discussion of boat building metals will be provided.

REASONS FOR SPECIFICATIONS

One of the first tasks of the designer is to compile a list of the owner's intentions. This is not only necessary for the designer to complete the drawings but the builder must know exactly what materials he will be using and what to charge for their fabrication. Most of the specifications are repeated on the construction drawings and this duplication of effort is necessary to describe every item prior to the construction phase. This avoids any misunderstanding as to exactly what the owner expects the builder to accomplish. Each type of material, surface finish and equipment that is permanently attached to the hull must be described.

Attached to the specifications is a list of equipment and hardware that will be purchased by the owner and installed by the builder. Sometimes, everything will be bought by the builder but frequently an owner feels he can purchase an item at lower cost. An owner may want equipment and fittings from his own country, which may not be available in the country in which the boat is built Specifications are necessary for a custom boat but are not usually written for a manufacturer as they have their own proven methods and materials. Often, a manufacturer will use the same hardware and interior finishes for every boat length they build.

Specifications are usually an integral part of the contract between the owner and the builder and include the following:

DECK EQUIPMENT

Number and type of anchors. Chain, Nylon or a combination of both for anchor rode.

Type of anchor windlass.

Aft windlass for dock lines?

Navigation lights (AC and DC).

Searchlight.

Do not use hardware of cast zinc.

Type and location of tender, davits and life raft.

Boarding ladders from the dock and from the water.

Storage for PFD's, life ring, fenders, dock lines.

Type and height of railings (lifelines).

Type of toe rail, scuppers, handrail on house.

Width of side decks.

Type of deck hatches and windows.

Deck material for a non-skid surface.

Hatches for engine removal.

Type of door to deck house, security alarms, locks.

Type of surface finish on the deck house.

Type of vents to the interior and to the engineroom.

HULLSIDE

Color and surface finish.

Color of boot top.

Type and location of rub rail.

Portlights to be non-opening.

STATEROOMS

Type of ceiling (headliner) under beams.
Type of hullside covering and floor covering.
Type of surface finish on interior bulkheads.
Type of natural ventilation and A/C ducts.
Type of mattresses.
Storage under beds.
Lamps.
Type of heat insulation outboard and overhead.
Type of sound insulation on bulkheads.

GALLEY

Fuel type and manufacturer of range.
Type of icebox or refrigerator.
Type of sink, dishwasher, microwave.
Location of trash bin.
Counter top material.
Number of drawers and cabinets.
Lighting.
Size of dining table and material.
Storage for plates and silver.
Type of flooring.

ELECTRICAL SYSTEMS

Voltage of circuits in the boat. AC and DC.
Electrical grounding system.
Only tinned copper wire to be used.
Wiring inside conduit?
Type of batteries for engines, house and generators.
Number and type of generators.
Number and type of circuit breakers.

Location and amperage of AC outlets in every compartment. Use three in every stateroom and in galley.

Type of light fixtures in staterooms, passageways.

Instrumentation at the helm station.

ENGINEROOM EQUIPMENT

List the manufacturer and model number of all engines and equipment shown on Figure 13-1. Boats over 60 feet (18.3 m) would have twice the amount of equipment in the engineroom.

Size of ventilation opening above the sheer.

Size of intake and exhaust air blowers.

Material for shafts, bearings, struts, propellers.

Hatches for engine removal.

PIPING SYSTEMS

Use steel piping in a steel hull and aluminum piping in an aluminum hull. Space hangars a maximum distance of 39 inches apart. (1.0 m). Through-hull fittings must be the same as the hull material.

A wood, glass fiber or ferro-cement boat can use a variety of piping material but care must be taken to use the same material throughout the system. Use bronze through-hull fittings for these type hulls. Use two hose clamps at each end of a hose. Use a fuel or hot water compatible hose to attach piping to a steel engine.

Do not use any reducing elbows in any part of the sea water piping, especially not at the strainer. Bottom grass and mud get trapped at the elbows. Bilge pumps must be located in each watertight compartment and are accessible through a hatch. Bilge pumps to have warning lights at helm to indicate when in operation.

All piping through watertight bulkheads must have watertight seals. (Stuffing Boxes)

HEADS

Type of toilet with a discharge to a holding tank and a provision for pumping out.

Type of sink and faucets.

Cabinets and drawers.

Type of shower enclosure.
Drain to a pump or tank.

INTERIOR IN GENERAL

Type of surface finish for all bulkheads, partitions, overhead, cabin sole and the outboard hull side.
Type of cabin sole (floor) hatches.
How are tanks removed?
Type of drawers. Lift to open with a finger slot?
Type of interior doors and surface finish. Flush locks?
Type of clothes washer and dryer.
Water trap type vents in all passageways and heads.
Lockers for linens, oilskins and boots.
Type of steering, helm electronics and engine controls.
Type of chart desk, electronics and chart storage.

DISSIMILAR METALS

It is important to know what materials to use when selecting boat hardware so electrochemical action does not corrode the metals. When some dissimilar metals are used in close proximity to each other, one is corroded and the other is protected. This is called galvanic corrosion, which is dependent on the area of each metal in addition to the type of metal. As an example, the use of a bronze propeller on a steel hull that has many zinc plates on top of the steel. The interaction of these three metals will be explained. It is important to use the correct metals and to list them in the written boat specifications.

The following list starts with the most protected metals at the top and has the most corroded metals at the bottom:
Mercury
Graphite (Carbon)
Platinum
Titanium
Type 316 Stainless Steel, Passivated
Nickel - Copper Alloys (Inconel®)
Type 302 and 304 Stainless Steel, Passivated

Silver
Lead _____
Copper - Nickel Alloys (Monel®)
Bronze Alloys
Brass Alloys
Copper
Tin
Stainless Steel Alloys, Active, no surface treatment.
Mild Steel and Cast Iron
Aluminum Alloys
Zinc and Galvanized Steel
Magnesium

Starting at the top of the above list, mercury compounds have been given wide news coverage as to their toxicity. They have since been banned from all paints and other commercial use. Mercury is so dangerous even thermometers containing mercury are forbidden. It is also corrosive to all other metals.

Carbon compounds are found everywhere but in the solid state they are very corrosive and act similar to other metals in that they are very good conductors of electricity. If graphite packing is used in the propeller shaft stuffing box, the shaft will be pitted Some years ago, bottom paint containing graphite was on the market for a few months, claiming to be very slippery on racing hulls. Pitting quickly developed on the propellers and shafts and the product was discontinued.

High quality stainless steels have a surface treatment with chemicals to reduce the chance of corrosion. These are found in the best propeller shafts, deck hardware and lifeline stanchions. Since the surface area of these parts is small compared with the area of the deck or hull, the corrosion potential is limited and they can be used on steel and aluminum hulls. The same explanation describes the use of bronze propellers on steel and aluminum hulls and blocks of zinc are used in both cases. The zinc blocks are corroded quickly, before the hull material, as they are on the bottom of the metals list. When you see the zincs disappear, it is time to replace them to preserve the hull.

The metal alloys containing Nickel and Copper are made in various formulations (Inconel and Monel are trademarks) and are primarily used for tubing in engine heat exchangers or air conditioning condensers. The best quality plastic or bronze fittings should be used with this equipment as brass fittings from some sources have recently been found to be of the wrong alloy.

Bronze alloys contain copper, tin and zinc and have proven to be the most durable of the metals. Ancient wrecks reveal perfectly preserved statues, fittings and cannon of bronze and copper, while the cast iron parts have been corroded to extinction. This proves the enduring lesson that copper and bronze cannot be used with steel or aluminum. The two lines on the metals list show only the middle grouping of compatible metals where few problems are encountered. Stainless steel propeller shafts and bronze propellers can be used on any boat.

Steel and Aluminum hulls are common but are always subject to corrosion problems. It is always best to use steel fittings and hardware on a steel hull and aluminum components on an aluminum hull. Stainless steel bolts are usually used on metal hulls and if a bronze fitting is installed on these hulls, a plastic washer plate must separate the two metals. Zinc blocks must be fastened to the keel area from bow to stern and around the propeller shaft strut and at the rudder posts.

Steel and aluminum are also subject to corrosion by oxidation (rust and aluminum oxide). When the two metals are put together without a plastic washer plate, the oxidation of each combines to form a very tight bond. During one project, I had a crane pulling on an aluminum mast to remove it from a sailboat, which unfortunately had a steel mast step. When the bow of the boat started to rise from the water, it was obvious there was a problem! After the steel mast step was unbolted from the keel structure, the mast step could only be removed from the mast by repeated heavy blows with a ten pound (4.54 kg) hammer.

Steel and aluminum hulls are also corroded by stray electrical currents in the water around piers and by an imperfect ground wire in the shore power electric supply. The latter is corrected by installing an isolation (1:1) transformer in the shore power wiring so that the ground wires are separated. Stray currents are detected by a hull potential meter and by rapidly dissolving zinc blocks, indicating the boat must be moved from the area.

SUMMARY

Careful selection of metal hardware is important to prevent corrosion. Bronze alloys, copper and stainless steel are used together as well as mild steel and non-passivated stainless steel or aluminum and stainless steel. An aluminum deck house on a steel hull can be installed with a plastic washer plate between the metals. All of this is included in the written specifications, which show the owner's intentions in all areas of the boat.

CHAPTER FIVE

CALCULATION OF WEIGHTS LONGITUDINAL CENTER OF GRAVITY VERTICAL CENTER OF GRAVITY

Weight is what makes a boat slow, sit at an angle that is not level and may even cause a boat to capsize if it is too high. Therefore, it is vital to know how much the boat will weigh and where the center of that weight is located. This chapter will show the procedure for determining these weight factors.

The styling drawing shows the boat profile exactly as the owner wants to see it. If the boat is too heavy, the actual waterline of flotation is changed, the freeboard is reduced and the owner has a visual disaster. The law of flotation says a floating body displaces its own weight of water. Therefore, if you know the total boat weight (displacement) is 64,000 pounds (29,056 kg), you divide by the weight of sea water (64 pounds per cuft) (1025 kg/m³) to get a required underwater volume of the hull of 1000 cuft (28.32 m³). When we draw the lines of the hull in *Chapter Nine*, they must enclose this exact volume and the center of this volume is the longitudinal center of buoyancy (LCB). You must have exact hull weight.

LEVEL TRIM

If the boat is going to float in level trim and at the correct waterline, the center of the total boat weight (Longitudinal Center of Gravity - LCG) must be carefully calculated. Then, the geometric center of the hull volume (Longitudinal Center Of Buoyancy - LCB) must be at the same fore-and-aft (longitudinal) position as the LCG. These principles of weight and trim apply equally to all lengths and types of hulls, whether it is a 33 foot (10 m) sailboat, a 60 foot (18.3 m) sport fisherman or a 100 foot (30.5 m) passenger ferry.

Level trim must also be considered in the athwartships position. Each item in the boat that is off the boat's centerline has its weight multiplied by the distance off centerline to get a heeling force to port or starboard. The total of the forces to each side must be equal if the boat is to float without a list.

Temporary weights of fish or deck cargoes must be secured from movement to each side. Tanks should be located port or starboard but never all the way across the hull, to prevent liquid movement with each roll of the boat. Tanks on the centerline are permissible.

Fuel and water should be located close to the LCG (near the middle of the boat) so there is little change in fore-and-aft trim from full to empty tanks. This requirement usually means the engineroom is located in the aft portion of the hull.

REFERENCE DIMENSIONS

The reference point for the longitudinal (fore-and-aft) position of the center of gravity (LCG) can be anywhere along the hull length. It is most convenient to use the vertical sections (stations) as established for the drawing of the hull lines and other calculations. These are equally spaced along the waterline length and the intersection of the stem and waterline is usually denoted as zero. For ease of calculation, an even number of spaces is used, normally ten on boats up to fifty feet (15.25 m) waterline length. Any even number of equal spaces may be used and the accuracy is greater with a large number of stations. This station spacing is established on the styling and arrangement drawings to get the locations noted on the weight calculations. In Figure 5-1, one-tenth of the station number is used to keep the numbers small for ease of calculation. Thus 0.65 means halfway between station 6 and 7. In other terms, this is 65 percent of the waterline length aft of station zero.

SAMPLE WEIGHT CALCULATION SUMMARY					
Item	Weight pounds	0.1 x Station Location	LCG Moment Wt x Station	Feet above base	VCG Moment Wt x Ft
37.5 ft lwl glass fiber hull	5,400	0.54	2,916	3.2	17 280
Transom & swim platform	460	1.01	465	4.5	2 070
8 Longitudinals	640	0.6	384	1.5	960
Peak bulkhead	60	0	0	5	300
Bulkhead at head	120	0.15	18	4	480
Fwd engineroom bulkhead	150	0.48	72	305	525
Aft engineroom bulkhead	150	0.75	113	3.5	525
Deck & beams	2,200	0.52	1,144	8.5	18 700
Fwd deck hardware	400	0.1	40	10	4 000
Aft deck hardware	100	0.9	90	7.5	750
Helm controls & console	500	0.5	250	8	4 000
Deck house lounge	650	0.65	423	7	4 550
Fwd berths	200	0.04	8	4	800
Head & lockers	700	0.2	140	3.5	2 450
Stateroom & cabin sole	700	0.31	217	4	2 800
Galley & sole	600	0.65	390	3.8	2 280
2 Engines & battery	7,300	0.61	4,453	3.7	27 010
Exhaust & piping	300	0.7	210	3.5	1 050
Pumps & filters	200	0.65	130	1.5	300
Shafts & seals	450	0.8	360	1	450
Struts & props	150	0.92	138	0.5	75
Rudders & steering	200	0.96	192	1.5	300
Electric panel & rect.	380	0.4	152	4	1 520
Wiring & fixtures	120	0.51	61	4.5	540
Plumbing, paint, trim	220	0.35	77	2	440
Crew & gear	1,800	0.7	1,260	5	9 000
Fuel - ½ tank	2,000	0.61	1,220	Fuel & water not included to get highest VCG	
Water - ½ tank	1,200	0.4	480		
Operating Weight	27,350	0.56	15,403	4.21	103,155

Figure 5-1 -- *Refer to Figures 11-1, 11-2, 11-3.*

LCG=15403 / 27350=.563 station. LCG is 56.3% of the waterline length aft of station zero. VCG=103155 / 24500=4.21ft Without fuel or water. The lines of the hull are drawn so the geometric center of the underwater volume, below the designed waterline, (Center of Buoyancy-CB) is at station .563. This must be the same as the LCG, above.

WEIGHT GROUPS

Figure 5-1 is an example of how the weights are tabulated. Once a designer calculates the area of a bulkhead, a cabinet or a berth and multiplies the volume by the density of the material, the procedure becomes easy. The middle of the length of an item can usually be taken as the position of the center of gravity. The weight of manufactured items may be found in the catalogs. The entire weight calculation may be on one page for a small boat or on thirty pages for a 100 foot (30.5 m) motor yacht. For convenience, the weight calculation is organized into the following categories, to suit the individual designer:

HULL: Longitudinal Frames, Hull Shell, Engine Girders, Bulkheads, Keel & Ballast, Transverse Frames.

DECK: Deck Plating, Hardware & Winches, Deck Beams, Hatches, Rub Rail, Tenders & Davits, Hand rails, Lines & Fenders, Fishing Gear, Anchor & Windlass.

SUPERSTRUCTURE: Bridge, Deck House Sides (4), Windows, Roof, Mast, Antennae, Lights, Horn.

SAILBOATS: Masts, Booms, Sails, Rigging, Poles, Wire Rope, Turnbuckles, Chainplates.

BRIDGE INTERIOR: Helm Controls, Steering, Electronics, Chart Desk.

MAIN DECK INTERIOR: Dining & Seating, Lounges & Bar, Galley, Stairs & Ladders, Deck Covering, Hullsides Covering, Lighting Fixtures, Window Covering, Owner's Stateroom, Laundry & Linen, Joiner Bulkheads, Bilge Pumps, Galley Stores.

HULL INTERIOR: Crew Berths & Heads, Guest Berths & Heads, Deck Covering, Overhead Covering, Hullside Covering.

ENGINEROOM: Engines & Reduction Gears, Engine Girders, Shafts & Bearings, Fuel & Water Tanks, Air Blowers, Watermaker, Bilge Pumps, Batteries, Propeller & Struts, Generators & Elect. Panel, Exhausts, Rudders & Steering, Air Conditioning, Lube Oil Tank, Piping Manifolds, Shore Power, Hot Water Tank, Pressure Water Pump.

The weights shown on Figure 5-1 are grouped together for simplification but are actually totals of carefully noted weights of individual items. For example, a propeller may be 39 pounds (17.7 kg) located at station .93. The shaft strut may be 36 pounds (16.3 kg), including bolts and a backing plate, located at station .91. Combined, two propellers and two shaft struts would weigh 150 pounds at station 0.92. The weights are taken from manufacturer's catalogs.

Similarly, a small sailboat may have a berth and shelf both to port and to starboard, with a table on the centerline. All the centers of gravity are at the same longitudinal and vertical location. These are noted on the weight list as "Berths and Table: 280 at .47". Some designers prefer to list each item separately, which improves the clarity but extends the list and the time required for completion. All designers file the weights of built-in joinerwork as well as loose furniture that has been calculated or weighed. A few of these items are noted in Figure 5-2.

The vertical location of the total center of gravity (VCG) of each part in the hull is noted at this time for convenience but it does not have to be on the same sheet as the LCG for each part. The VCG is used in the stability calculations of *Chapter Ten.* The water line of the styling drawing or other convenient base line, can be used as a reference for the heights of each item.

The determination of ballast weight will be made in *Chapter Ten* during the discussion of stability. For preliminary weight estimates, the ballast weight may be assumed at thirty percent of total displacement for cruising sailboats and forty percent for racing hulls.

The lines of the hull are drawn so the geometric center of the underwater volume, below the designed waterline, (Center of Buoyancy - CB) is at station .563, which must be the same as the LCG, above.

FURNITURE WEIGHT IN POUNDS		
Hollow door	w/locks & hinges	34
Mirror	20 x 26 w/frame	13
Drawer 16 x 23 x 5	Empty Full	10 15
Chest of 5 drawers 18 x 30 x 46	Full	165
Sofa 35 x 80 35 x 80	Standard Convertible to bed	120 245
Chair	Upholstered Light Upholstered Heavy Dining	32 47 22
Table	Dining 36 x 54 Mahogany 36 x 36 x 30 Coffee 22 x 50 light wood End 18 x 27 light wood Night stand 14 x 16 full	95 51 27 23 32
Single bed 36 x 78	Foam mattress 6" Cotton mattress 6" Box spring Solid wood frame/headboard Steel angle frame/no head board	23 41 60 42 20
Queen bed 60 x 80	Foam mattress 6" Cotton mattress 6" Box spring Solid wood frame/headboard Steel angle frame/no head board	34 70 80 28 36
Carpet lb/sqft	Plush Pad Area rug Vinyl tile	.58 .30 .41 .26
Fir plywood	Pounds per cuft 1" Thick pounds per sqft 1/2" Thick pounds per sqft	36 3 1.5

Figure 5-2

Weights of hardware & appliances can be found in the catalogs.

AREAS OF CURVED SURFACES AND SIMPSON'S RULE

To list the weight of each item in the boat you must have the curved hull surface area (shell) and the area of the curved decks. Other curved areas must be calculated such as waterplane areas, hull volume (displacement) and ballast volume. Those who design with computers will have programs to do these area and volume calculations but the reasoning behind the procedure should be explained.

Figure 5-3 shows one-half of a waterline shape (waterplane) with equally spaced stations, dividing the area into an even number of parts. The linear length at each station represents the half beam of the waterplane, carefully drawn to scale. If you average the lengths of two adjacent stations and multiply by the station spacing, you have the area between those two stations. Adding this area for all pairs of stations gives the area of the waterplane.

Another method for this calculation uses Simpson's Rule by multiplying the waterline width at each station by one of following numbers (1,4,2,4,2, etc. 4,2,4,1). The first and last station is multiplied by one and the second and second last station is multiplied by four. The total of these is multiplied by one-third the station spacing to get waterplane area. If only one-half of the waterplane beam is used, to one side of centerline, the result is doubled. When the center of gravity of this area is desired, the previous list of numbers is multiplied by the station number (not the station spacing). The total of this list is divided by the total of the previous list to get the LCG, in terms of the station numbers.

When the area of the hull surface is desired (the shell), you use the same calculation as above but entering the girth from keel to chine (or turn of the bilge) to sheer at each station, instead of the beam. The stations are established on the waterline length and the calculation for hull area must be expanded to include the area forward of station "0" and aft of the stern station. This may be done by direct measurement or by using two or four additional stations. In both cases, be sure to add the area of the transom, across the stern.

The calculation of section area at each station is done by a mechanical device called a planimeter or by a computer program. Each section area is used in the above calculations to get hull volume (displacement) below the desired waterline. Each section area can be found manually by dividing the area into stations, equally spaced and using the above methods. As an alternative, each section area can be divided into right triangles and the areas added. The area of any right triangle is one-half the multiplication of the length of two sides. This is shown in Figure 5-3.

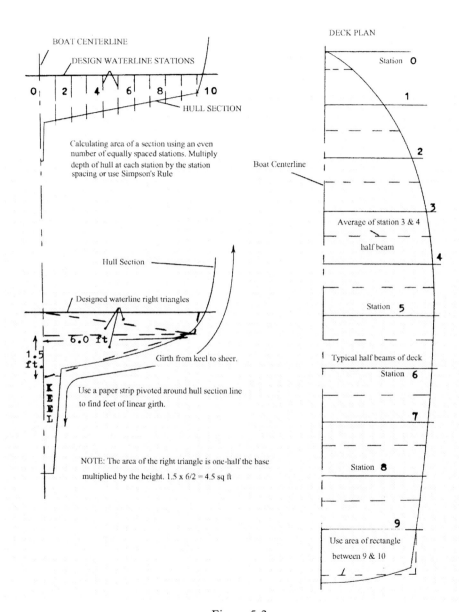

BOAT CENTERLINE

DESIGN WATERLINE STATIONS

0   2   4   6   8   10

HULL SECTION

Calculating area of a section using an even
number of equally spaced stations. Multiply
depth of hull at each station by the station
spacing or use Simpson's Rule

Hull Section

Designed waterline right triangles

6.0 ft

1.5 ft

Girth from keel to sheer.

K
E
E
L

Use a paper strip pivoted around hull section line
to find feet of linear girth.

NOTE: The area of the right triangle is one-half the base
multiplied by the height. 1.5 x 6/2 = 4.5 sq ft

DECK PLAN

Station 0

1

2

Boat Centerline

3

Average of station 3 & 4

half beam

4

Station 5

Typical half beams of deck

Station 6

7

Station 8

9

Use area of rectangle
between 9 & 10

Figure 5-3

Calculating areas of curved surfaces.

CHANGES IN BOAT WEIGHT

When there is a wide variation in boat weight, as with a fishing vessel, cargo boat or a passenger vessel, you must know how much weight will lower the hull how much further in the water. This is called "Per Inch Immersion". For safety reasons, any boat's freeboard at light weight should never be reduced by more than half. The design principles are the same for all hull applications.

The area of the desired waterline (designed waterline) or any other, is multiplied by the density of sea (or fresh) water and then divided by 12 inches in a foot if in the English system. Since hull sides are tapered, this value must be found every three inches (76.2 cm) of draft. For example, a waterplane area of 300 sqft (27.9 m^2) divided by 12 and multiplied by 64 lb/ft^3 (1025 kg/m^3) (density of salt water) would give an immersion value of 1600 lbs per inch (28597 kg per meter), in sea water.

SUMMARY

The weight and center of gravity of each item in the boat is extremely important to the whole design. Every phase of the design process is based on weight and trim and errors with either factor cannot be tolerated.

CHAPTER SIX

BOATBUILDING MATERIALS & SCANTLINGS

The material for any boat is usually determined by the preference of the owner, who considers durability, price and availability. This chapter will discuss the properties of each material and the methods used to find the correct thickness. Some calculations are necessary but they involve only number substitution in formulae and can be accomplished with a common calculator. It can be dangerous to compare the hull thickness and hull stiffener (framing) size of one boat with another unless they are very close in size, speed and intended use. This is why calculations are required for each hull.

HULL WEIGHT

The tables of hull thickness and stiffener (framing) size in this chapter can be used to make a weight evaluation of all boatbuilding materials. If you add the hull and stiffener weight over a length that includes one transverse stiffener (Web Frame), you will find a wood, aluminum and glass fiber hull have about equal weight. A steel hull is about twice this weight and a ferro-cement hull is about twice the weight of a steel hull. These comparisons are approximate but they do indicate the proper relationships.

When considering racing sailboats or high speed powerboats, weight becomes a critical factor but displacement speed craft (slower boats) can use any material that is economical. High speed always demands light weight in any vehicle, whether it is aircraft, car or boat.

CRITERIA FOR SELECTION OF A BOAT MATERIAL

The following questions must be considered when selecting a boatbuilding material:
a. Is the builder skilled in this material?
b. Is the material readily available?
c. What is the corrosion resistance?
d. What is the longevity of the material?
e. Is the material cost and cost of labor critical?
f. What maintenance is required?
g. Can this material be used within local regulations?

In highly industrialized countries, almost every material is available and a qualified builder can be found. The owner can then select whatever material fits his needs and desires. When a small, isolated, country is considered, there are problems of the high cost of importing materials, an unskilled labor force and the need to generate electrical power for welding using expensive imported fuel.

DESIGN PRESSURE

Before considering the sizes of materials (scantlings) for the hull, we must know the design pressure to which the hull is subjected. This varies with the size of the hull, hull weight and speed. In an attempt to simplify the determination of design pressure for small craft over a wide range of speeds, I have measured the hull thickness, framing, weight and speed of many successful hulls. The following formula was developed from this data and is presented in Figure 6-1.

$P = .015 (V^2) + .2 (Disp^{.33}) + .04$ LWL (English units) where P is pounds per square inch (psi), V is in knots, LWL is waterline length in feet, Displacement is in cubic feet.

$P = .03 (V^2) + .25 (Disp^{.33}) + 1.3$ LWL (SI units) where P is kilo Pascals (kPa), V is in km per hour, LWL is waterline length in meters (m), Displacement is kilograms (kg).

The above formula is only to be used with hulls less than 120ft (36.6 m) water-line and it is for the bottom of the hull only. The hullside design pressure is 75% of the bottom pressure but not less than 3 psi (20.7 kPa). 50% of the hull bottom design pressure can be used for hull framing. Local loads of equipment and cargo are in addition to the hull bottom design pressure. The minimum pressure of 3 psi (20.7 kPa) also applies to decks and superstructures.

Some of the heaviest loads a hull may encounter are on a trailer being hauled over a rough road. When a boat is hauled out of the water and is sitting on two or three keel blocks, the keel may be crushed if it is only the same thickness as the hull bottom. For these reasons, the keel area or fully built-up keel, should be twice the thickness of the hull bottom, over an area of one foot on (305mm) both sides of the boat centerline.

Cracks have developed in the bow area of glass fiber hulls in both sailboats and powerboats after continued pounding into a head sea and this can occur at any portion of the hull length. For this reason, the hull bottom thickness and the bow areas should be equal throughout the hull length.

CALCULATION OF HULL BOTTOM THICKNESS

A section of the hull bottom between frames (stiffeners) acts like a uniformly loaded beam with fixed ends. The formula for the calculated bending of this beam can be found in any engineering handbook and is called the bending moment (BM). This factor is used to calculate the required stiffness of the beam to resist bending. This stiffness is designated Section Modulus (SM) (in^3 or cm^3) or the stiffness of the beam may be called Moment Of Inertia (I) (in^4 or cm^4). The difference between these two names is a linear measurement from the outer edge of the beam to the line of zero bending (Neutral Axis) (y), near the middle portion of the beam. Thus, SM = I / y. This neutral axis exists as one edge of the beam is in tension and the other edge is in compression, when the beam is bent by a load.

Bending Moment: BM = P (L^2) / 12 (Fixed Ends) where P is hull design pressure and L is the spacing between frames. (Basic beam bending formula)

The required Section Modulus is SM = BM / S, where S is the allowable stress of the material (psi or kPa). Consider a one inch (one mm) wide strip of the hull bottom as the beam, where the Section Modulus (SM) of the rectangle is; $SM = bt^2 / 6$, where t is the thickness and b is one inch (1 mm). Combine the above formulas to find hull thickness on the hull bottom: $SM = t^2 / 6 = PL^2 / 12 \, S$ and $t^2 = PL^2 / 2 \, S$. This is the required hull thickness resulting from a pressure being applied over an area supported on four sides by stiffeners (framing).

SAMPLE HULL THICKNESS CALCULATION

If a 32.5 foot (9.9 m) waterline length (LWL) aluminum hull is moving at 22 KT (40.8 km/hr), the hull design pressure is 10 psi (68.9 kPa). Assume a frame spacing of 20 inches (508 mm) and the allowable yield strength of aluminum is 18,000 psi (124,000 kPa). The required hull thickness is: $t^2 = PL^2 / 2 \, S$

$t^2 = 10 \times 400 / 36{,}000 = .111$ and $t = .333$ inches (8.5 mm)

When the bottom of the hull is subjected to a load, it flexes and this movement must be limited to a commonly accepted value of 0.02 multiplied by the frame spacing. To measure this movement, a calculation for deflection is made, using the flexural modulus (E) of the particular material. This latter value is a ratio of the stress in a material when subjected to a load that produces a percentage change in elongation of the material, expressed in psi or kPa. For aluminum, the flexural modulus (E) is 10×10^6 psi (68.9×10^6 kPa). This value is 1.3×10^6 for glass fiber laminates and 30×10^6 psi (207×10^6 kPa) for steel.

The deflection (d) formula is $d = P \, (L^4) / 384 \, E \, I$, where E is the flexural modulus and I is the moment of inertia of the beam under investigation. The moment of inertia of a rectangular section is $bt^3 / 12 = I$ and the 0.333 in (8.5 mm) plating has $I = 1 \times .333^3 / 12 = .003 \ in^4$ (1249 mm^4). Deflection (d) is therefore:

$d = 10 \, (20^4) / 384 \, (10 \times 10^6) \, .003 = .139$ in (3.5 mm).

This deflection is limited to $.02 \times 20$ in $= 0.4$ in (10.2 mm). Since the calculated deflection is less than this value, the hull bottom thickness is satisfactory. If the calculated deflection is greater than the maximum allowed, the calculation is repeated, using a greater hull thickness, until the deflection is satisfactory.

HULL STIFFENERS (FRAMING)

The example above assumes the hull plating to be supported every 20 inches (508 mm) with longitudinal or transverse (web) frames or a combination of both. The designer arranges the framing spacing and type to achieve light weight or minimum welding length or the custom of the builder. The method of calculation is the same for all types of hull stiffeners, with any material. Only for purposes of illustration and with the exception of wood hulls, the examples in this chapter assume the transverse (web) stiffeners to be 96 in (2440 mm) apart, which may be bulkheads in the boat. The longitudinal stiffeners are assumed to be 20 in (508 mm) apart.

The examples in this chapter also make the assumption of the length of the transverse (web) framing (keel to chine):

WATERLINE LENGTH OF HULL			ASSUMED LENGTH OF TRANSVERSE		
20	ft	(6.1 m)	50	in	(1270 mm)
30	ft	(9.15 m)	60	in	(1524 mm)
40	ft	(12.2 m)	70	in	(1778 mm)
50	ft	(15.25 m)	80	in	(2032 mm)
75	ft	(22.9 m)	90	in	(2286 mm)
100	ft	(30.5 m)	100	in	(2540 mm)

Since the span of the transverse (web) frames and frame spacing vary with each hull, the scantlings must be individually calculated for each hull. The tables of hull thickness and hull framing presented in this book vary with local loads, frame spacing and installed equipment. Each designer is responsible for his calculations for any particular hull. The author and publisher are not responsible for the application of this data by others.

Moment of Inertia and Section Modulus are measurements of resistance to movement of a particular shape. These values and methods of calculation may be found in an engineering handbook for angles, tees, I-beams or other shapes. The size of these shapes is investigated after the calculations for required Section Modulus have been completed. The calculations for required Section Modulus are applied to that value for the combined frame and hull plating thickness. The Moment of Inertia used in the deflection calculation is for the shape of the frame, only. The sample calculations will use the same aluminum hull as previously mentioned. The design pressure for framing is half that of the hull bottom.

TRANSVERSE (WEB) FRAMES
(Used with longitudinal frames)

The spacing assumed is 96 in (2440 mm) and the yield strength of aluminum is 18,000 psi (124,000 kPa). The design pressure is 5 psi (34.4 kPa), half that of the hull bottom pressure. The approximate length of the transverse frame, from keel to chine, is 80 in (2040 mm). The required Section Modulus for framing is:

$SM = PsL^2 / 12S$.
$SM = 5 (96) 6400 / 12 (18000) = 14.2$ in^3 (235 cm^3).
Use an aluminum angle with a slightly larger Section Modulus.
Use 8 in x 6 in x .25 in (SM = 14.3 in^3).
Use 203.5 mm x 152 mm x 6.3 mm (SM = 235 cm^3).

The moment of inertia of this angle is 23 in^4 (957 cm^4). The angle is positioned with the short dimension away from the hull and the long dimension in a vertical plane. This framing is shown in Figure 11-5. The deflection of this frame is:

$d = PsL^4 / 384$ E I.
$d = 5 (96) 804 / 384 (10 \times 10^6) 23 = .223$ in (5.66 mm)

The maximum allowable deflection for framing is the length of the frame divided by 100. In this case, 80 / 100 = .8 in (20.4 mm) is maximum and the calculated deflection of .223 in (5.66 mm) is satisfactory, as it is less than 0.8 in

LONGITUDINAL FRAMES
(Used with transverse frames)

The spacing is 20 in (508 mm) and the length is 96 in (2438 mm).
$SM = PsL^2 / 12$ S
$SM = 5 (20) 96^2 / 12 (18000) = 4.27$ in^3 (70 cm^3).
Use an aluminum angle 5 x 3 x .25 in (127 x 76 mm) where the SM = 4.9 in^3 (81cm^3) and I = 5.0 in^4 (208 cm^4)
Deflection (d) = $PsL^4 / 384$ E I
$d = 5 (20) 96^4 / 384 (10 \times 10^6) 5 = .442$ in (11.2 mm).
This deflection is less than .01 x 96 = .96 in (24.4 mm) and is satisfactory.

ALL TRANSVERSE FRAMING
WITHOUT LONGITUDINAL FRAMES

As before, the example aluminum hull has a spacing(s) of 20 in (508 mm) and L = 80 in (2030 mm). $SM = Psl^2 / 12s$

$SM = 5 (20) 80^2 / 12 (18000) = 2.96 in^3 (48.5 cm^3)$
Use an aluminum angle 4 x 3 x .25 in (102 x 76 x 6 mm) where the
$SM = 3.7 in^3 (60.6 cm^3)$ and $I = 2.7 in^4 (112.3 cm^4)$.
The deflection $d = PsL^4 / 384 E I$
$d = 5 (20) 80^4 / 384 (10 x 10^6) 2.7 = 0.395 in (10 mm)$
This deflection is less than .01 x 80 = .8 in (20.35 mm) and it is satisfactory.

WEIGHT COMPARISON OF FRAMING TYPES

It is valuable to compare the weight of all transverse framing with that of the combination of longitudinal and transverse (web) frames. This comparison may vary with the hull material and length of hull and a general conclusion cannot be made. Each hull should be calculated.

All Transverse Framing: Using the above example, a hull length of 96 in (2438 mm) will have five transverse frames, each with a section area of 1.75 in² (11.3 cm²). This weight, on each side of the boat, is 5 x 1.75 x 80 x 165lb/cuft divided by 1728, which is 66.8 pounds (30.3 kg). The length of the framing to be stagger welded is 400 inches (1016 cm).

Longitudinal and Transverse Framing: In the same length of hull section, there will be one transverse (web) frame with a section area of 3.5 in² (22.6 cm²). Its weight is 3.5 x 80 x 165 / 1728 = 26.7 pounds (12.1 kg) and there is 80 inches (203 cm) to be stagger welded. In addition, there are three longitudinals in a hull half width of 80 inches (203 cm), with each having a sectional area of 2.0 in² (12.9 cm²). Their weight is 3 x 2 x 96 x 165 / 1728 = 55 pounds (25 kg). There are 288 in (731.5 cm) to be welded. Adding the above, the total weight of this combination of framing is 81.7 pounds (37 kg). Therefore, the all transverse framing is 15 pounds (6.8 kg) lighter for a 96 inch (2438 mm) length of hull. But, there are 32 inches (81.3 cm) more welding required. Different lengths of hull should be investigated to determine the desired type of framing.

This concludes some examples of calculation of hull thickness and sizes of framing. The specific properties of each material will now be discussed.

ALUMINUM

The light weight of aluminum structures is appealing in all vessels, especially for superstructures above the main deck, where the lighter weight lowers the center of gravity with a resulting improvement in stability. Usually, aluminum hulls do not have to be painted on the inside and some boats are not painted on the outside, above the waterline but only when alloys are used that are resistant to salt water environments.

Photo 1

Photo 1 shows aluminum frames and a bulkhead set vertically on the round and flat bar keel. Note the frame cuts for the round bar chine and the flat bar side longitudinals. Bottom longitudinals are "T" shaped.

Alloys of aluminum are made for specific purposes such as casting, extruding, corrosion resistance and forming into structural shapes. Each application requires the careful selection of the correct alloy. Salt water use demands the alloy number beginning with "5" such as 5052 or 5086, which is not heat treatable. Extrusions of aluminum are usually made with the 6061 or 6063 alloy, which are subject to heat treatment.

The yield strength of the "5000" series of alloys is generally accepted at 18,000 psi (124,000 kPa) and the flexural modulus is 10×10^6 psi (68.9×10^6 kPa). The average density of aluminum is 165 lbs/cuft (2643 kg/m^3). Figures 6-2 and 6-3 show the hull bottom plating thickness and the sizes of framing for aluminum hulls. The aluminum plate and shapes are relatively high in cost compared with other boatbuilding materials but the light weight makes aluminum very desirable.

Stray electrical currents around piers will cause corrosion of the aluminum and many sacrificial zinc blocks as well as a hull potential meter should be used. Aluminum is low on the list of protected metals and only zinc and magnesium are lower. Bronze or brass fittings should never be used with aluminum but stainless steel is acceptable. Lead ballast must be insulated from the aluminum hull plating with a non-conductive plastic sheet such as Formica or Micarta (trademarks).

Photo 2

Photo 3

Photos 2 & 3 show aluminum bulkheads with "T" stiffeners, longitudinal deep angle deck supports, flanged plate bottom frames, transverse frames and keel.

STEEL

The widespread use of steel in many industries, combined with low cost and availability of welders, has made steel the worldwide favorite material for ship and commercial boat construction. Improper application of paint and the lack of continued maintenance on some ships, results in streaks of rust that small boat owners find objectionable. This lack of attention by some should not turn people away from steel. I have talked with some people who have cruised around the world and who would choose steel for their next boat hull. They have said the greatest danger to ocean cruising is the collision with floating boxes, logs and other flotsam. There are many alloys of steel, with strengths to match every purpose but mild steel at minimum cost is normally used in boat construction.

The calculations for steel hull thickness and framing are the same as for aluminum but using the proper values for yield strength and flexural modulus. The average yield strength for mild steel is 30,000 psi (207,000kPa) and the flexural modulus is 30 x 10^6 psi (207 x 106 kPa). An average density for steel is 490 pounds per cubic foot (7849 kg/m^3). Figures 6-4 and 6-5 show some examples of plate thickness and framing size for selected frame spacing and hull length. Calculations will have to be made for other frame spacings and other alloys of steel.

In addition to the problems of electrochemical corrosion, mentioned for aluminum, steel rusts very quickly and must be kept painted at all times. Any unpainted area should be sand blasted or wire brushed and have the primer applied immediately. Not more than four square feet (0.4m^2) should be cleaned and primed at one time. In the humid air of boat yards, steel will get a rust "bloom" on bare metal in a matter of minutes.

When taking electrical power from the shore on both steel and aluminum hulls, the connections should be made to an isolation transformer to avoid the difference in ground wire potential between the shore power and the boat's electrical system. Sacrificial zinc blocks must be installed every nine feet (2.74 m) along the keel.

The weight of steel hulls usually limits them to slower, displacement hulls but the low initial cost and worldwide availability of the material keep steel mills busy supplying shipyards and construction projects.

PLASTIC COMPOSITES

The use of reinforcing fibers in a resin binder forms the usual definition of "plastic composites" and there are many variations of each component. These are man-made laminates with widely varying properties dependent on the material used, the skill of the laminator and the technique of lamination. In manufacturing practice, the quality control may be very strict or non-existent. For these reasons, the strength of a laminate made in any shop can only be determined by having a sample tested in an engineering laboratory. This testing should be repeated every six months to insure the laminating crew has not changed their procedures.

PROPERTIES OF GLASS FIBER LAMINATES

Most manufacturers use glass fibers for reinforcing together with polyester resins as they are the least expensive and they will be illustrated in this chapter. The exterior of a boat hull, built in a mold, has special resin coatings called a "gel coat" that resists sunlight deterioration and prevents water migration into the laminate. The resin manufacturers are constantly improving these coatings and they should be consulted for the latest developments. Usually, boat hulls are made in an open mold with hand lay-up of the plies. The glass material is saturated with polyester resin and rolled with a stainless steel disc roller to insure the resin penetrates the reinforcing fabric. Other formulations of resins may be used.

The glass material normally used is the least expensive "E" glass in the form of 1.5 ounce per square foot (460 gm/m^2) "mat" with 0.050 in (1.27 mm) thickness per ply. This "mat" alternates with 19 ounces per square yard (647 gm/m^2) "woven roving", having 0.040 in (1 mm) thickness per ply. The lighter "mat" material results in a greater thickness per ply of finished laminate as it absorbs more resin. The completed laminate has a density about 96 pounds per cubic foot (1535 kg/m^3), an average flexural strength of 29,000 psi (200,000 kPa) and an average flexural modulus (E) of 1.3 x 10^6 psi (8.9 x 10^6 kPa). A factor of safety of two is used with the flexural strength. Factors of safety are used in engineering calculations when there may be variations or faults within the material. In a glass fiber laminate, the fibers may not have been saturated with resin or there may be internal checks or knots in a wood plank.

The ratio of glass fiber material to resin, by weight, varies considerably with each laminator and the resulting strength varies in proportion. You can expect 30%

to 40% glass in an average hand lay-up laminate. More critical laminates are made by covering the mold with a plastic sheet and pumping a vacuum between the sheet and the laminate (vacuum bagging). In this manner, 50% to 60% glass content may be realized as less resin is used to saturate the glass.

Photo 7

A glass fiber sailboat mold with steel pipe reinforcing on the outside. Steel frames allow the mold to be tilted to permit the laminators to stand on the floor to reach half of the hull.

Glass fiber pipe and specialized parts can be made with even higher glass content by filament winding. This is done by wrapping fibers soaked in resin over a rotating form (mandrel). Highly sophisticated machinery has been developed to produce parts with a glass fiber content of more than 70%. Other fibers can also use this method, with many different resins and laminate strengths.

Both custom and manufactured boats are built of glass fiber with well-deserved popularity. The hull is resistant to corrosion and maintenance is greatly reduced. Builders who can afford the high initial cost of molds, find the labor hours are less than with other materials and the completed boat can be sold at a competitive price.

Custom glass hulls built without a mold must be tediously sanded on the outside to achieve an acceptable surface finish. One exception to this is the custom, V-bottom hull fabricated from full length sheets of glass laminate that have the gel coat finish on one side.

There are a few problems with glass fiber hulls but they can be solved with careful fabrication and quality control. Ordinary resins can burn if a fire is started in the hull but fire-retardant resins are available. Any openings in the hull must be sealed with resin to prevent water migration into the edges of the laminate which may result in delamination.

SAMPLE CALCULATION FOR A GLASS FIBER HULL

The method of determining hull thickness and hull framing is the same as that used for an aluminum boat but a new calculation will be shown, since glass fiber boats are in such widespread use. Assume a 32.5ft (9.9 m) waterline length hull designed for 30 knots (55.7km/hr) of speed. The hull bottom design pressure is 16 psi (110 kPa) and the frame spacing is 20 in (508 mm).

<u>Hull Thickness</u> (t): $t^2 = PL^2$ divided by (/) 2S
$t^2 = 16 (20^2) / 2 (14,500)$, using a factor of safety of two.
$t^2 = .22$ and $t = .47$ in (12 mm)
$I = bt^3 / 12$: $I = .00865$ in^4 (3600 mm^4)
Deflection (d): $d = P L^4 / 384 E I$, where $E = (8.96 \times 10^6$ kPa)
$d = 16 (20^4) / 384 (1.3 \times 10^6) .00865 = .587$ in (15 mm)
Allowable deflection is $.02 \times 1 = .02 (20) = .4$ in (10 mm).

Since the deflection is greater than allowed, the calculation is repeated using a greater hull thickness. If the hull thickness is .55 in (14 mm); $I = bt^3 / 12$ and
$I = .166 / 12 = .0139$ in^4 (5786 mm^4)
$d = 16 (20^4) / 384 (1.3 \times 10^6) .0139 = .37$ in (9.4 mm)
This deflection is less than .4 in (10 mm) and is satisfactory.

Instructions to the builder have to be in terms of the number of plies of laminate as the hull thickness cannot be directly measured in a mold. One ply of 1.5oz (460 gm/m^2) mat and one ply of 19oz (647 gm/m^2) woven roving (a pair), would have a total thickness of .090 in (2.3 mm). Thus, the above example would use six pair plus the gel coat to get the required hull thickness. The ply thickness measurement will vary widely with the skill of the laminator and the quality control of the amount of resin used. The above numbers are averages that have been proven over many years. Thickness and laminate strength will also vary if more expensive resins are used, such as vinylester, epoxy and other newly developed resins. Different resins have varying chemical bonds with the reinforcing fibers.

Figures 6-6 and 6-7 show some examples of the hull thickness and frame sizes for glass fiber boats. The hull framing is calculated in the same manner as the previous example for aluminum hulls.

Transverse (web) Frames: The spacing is 96 in (2440 mm) and the frame length is about 60 in (1520 mm) in a 30 ft (9.lm) hull. The frame pressure is half the bottom pressure; use 8 psi (55 kPa). Flexural strength of glass fiber is 29,000 psi (200 MPa), divided by a factor of safety of 2.0. The required section modulus:

$Sm = PsL^2 / 12\ S.$
$SM = 8\ (96)\ 3600 / 12\ (14{,}500) = 15.9\ in^3\ (261\ cm^3)$

Select a solid glass rectangular section (flat bar) 8 in x 1 in (204 mm x 25.4 mm) as this shape is the easiest to fabricate in solid glass fiber laminate and is most commonly used by manufacturers. This shape has a section modulus of 17 in³ (279 cm³) and I = 42.6 in⁴ (1782 cm⁴).

Deflection (d): $d = PsL^4 / 384\ E\ I.$
$d = 8\ (96)\ 60^4 / 384\ (1.3\ x\ 10^6)\ 42.6 = .468\ in\ (12\ mm)$
Maximum allowable deflection is L / 100: 60 / 100 = .6 in (15.2 mm).
The deflection is less than 0.6 and is satisfactory.

Longitudinal frames: These longitudinal frames are used together with the transverse (web) frames mentioned above and are fabricated from solid glass fiber laminate. Their spacing is 20 in (508 mm) and the frame length is 96 inches (2440 mm). Required section Modulus :

$SN = PsL^2 / 12\ S.$
$SM = 8\ (20)\ 96^2 / 12\ (14{,}500) = 8.47\ in^3\ (139\ cm^3).$
Select a 6 in x 1 (152 mm x 25.4 mm) flat bar with SM = 9.5 in³ (156 cm³) and I = 18 in⁴ (756 cm⁴). The maximum deflection allowed is L / 100: 96 / 100 = .96 in (24.4 mm).
$d = PsL^4 / 384\ E\ I.$
$d = 8\ (20)\ 96^4 / 384\ (1.3\ x\ 10^6)\ 18 = 1.51\ in\ (384\ mm).$
This deflection is excessive and an 8 in x 1 in flat bar must be used (204 mm x 25.4 mm). This SM =17 in³ (279 cm³) and the I = 42.6 in⁴ (1782 cm⁴).
$d = 8\ (20)\ 964 / 384\ (1.3\ x\ 10^6)\ 42.6 = .639\ in\ (16\ mm).$
This deflection less than .96 in (24.4 mm) and is satisfactory.

LAMINATES WITH A CORE

With the objective of producing lighter hulls and decks, many designers and builders have been using a solid glass laminate on both sides of an internal core material (sandwich laminate). This replaces the entirely solid glass fiber and resin with a structure that is lighter but which has the same stiffness. One disadvantage is the outer laminates and core may be crushed under impact loading. Also, there are more hours required to fabricate a sandwich laminate.

It is not good practice to use a core material in a hull bottom as the laminate may be crushed when sitting on two keel blocks in a boatyard or when a boat is on a trailer and subjected to impact loading.

There are many core materials on the market but any used for boats must be light in weight, impervious to the migration of water throughout the core and have good chemical bonding to polyester resin. Some core materials in wide use are: urethane foam, polyvinyl chloride (PVC) foam, other plastic foams, end-grain balsa wood and various plastic or aluminum "honeycomb" shaped materials.

When using glass laminates on both sides of a core material, the following guidelines should he used:

a. Deck beams and hull side beams (framing) must be used and spaced as previously discussed for the hull.

b. A "mat" reinforcing ply must be used next to each side of the core material, to absorb sufficient resin.

c. Use a minimum of .36 in (9 mm) of total glass thickness; .18 in (4.5 mm) on each side of the core.

d. Use a minimum of .75 in (19 mm) of core thickness.

e. Total glass thickness should not be less than 80% of a solid glass laminate without a core.

Photo 12

A wood plug for a cruising sailboat. A core material will be laid on the plug and the outer laminate of glass applied on top of the core. After sanding the outside to obtain a fair surface, the plug is removed and the inside laminate is applied.

DECK LOADS AND LAMINATES

The loads experienced by a deck are not influenced by boat length or speed but by temporary loads and installed equipment. There must be supporting posts or bulkheads under tenders, davits, winches, reels, A-frames and other heavy gear. If a 210 pound (95 kg) person has a "footprint" area of 70 in² (450 cm²), the deck load is 3 psi (21 kPa). This is the minimum design pressure for decks, roofs and super-structures. The deck laminate thickness is calculated similarly to the hull bottom and is often the same as the hull bottom thickness if the bulkhead and stiffener spacing are wide.

Some glass fiber boat manufacturers abuse the use of core construction in a deck laminate by not using beams. This allows the deck to flex between bulkheads. When calculating the required thickness of a deck in such a hull, the total beam of the boat at that location will have to be used for "S", the stiffener spacing. After the solid glass thickness is found, 80% or .36 in (9 mm), whichever is greater, is used for the total glass thickness in a cored laminate.

Good engineering practice calls for the deck to be supported by attachment to the top of every bulkhead. This can be done in a glass fiber boat by using epoxy glue or by glass overlay between deck and bulkhead. This is especially important in a sailboat with the mast stepped on the keel. When sailing to windward, the slope of the windward shroud, in tension, pulls the windward sheer inboard. At the same time, the leeward sheer is supported by the water under the hull side. The resulting force pushes the deck or cabin top, upward if the deck is not secured to the bulkheads. Continued flexing in this manner causes cracks in the glass fiber deck. A "tie rod" of bronze or aluminum can be installed between the deck and the bottom framing to prevent this deck movement.

OTHER REINFORCING FIBERS

The examples given in this section on glass fiber laminates has mentioned only the "mat" and "woven roving" material but glass or other fibers, can be knitted or woven to form reinforcing fibers that have greater strength properties. Other fibers include "S" glass, aramid fibers, carbon fibers and other synthetic fibers. Each is laminated with high strength resins to get laminates of lighter weight with adequate strength. These high quality materials also have a higher price but are in demand for racing hulls and sailboat masts. These fibers can also be used with ordinary glass in areas where a higher strength reinforcement is required.

As with any laminate, the resulting material is manmade and the flexural strength varies with the skill of the laminator, percentage of fiber by weight, type of resin and the method of fabrication. Each builder should have his laminate tested so the designer will know what flexural strength to expect.

One example of special fiber weaves is the uni-directional fabric that has most of the material fibers arranged in one direction. This fabric may be used in areas where high strength is desired in one direction, such as sailboat rudders, masts and chainplates. A free standing sailboat mast does not have any rigging for support and it acts like a cantilevered beam with all the load in bending. If the mast is fabricated with uni-directional glass fabric laid lengthwise, the resulting flexural strength in greatly increased in this direction.

Some tests with uni-directional glass fiber laminates have reported flexural strengths of 55,000 psi (378 MPa) as compared with 29,000 psi (200 MPa) for an average hull laminate. This should not be interpreted to use uni-directional fabric so boat hulls can be thinner and lighter. We need hull strength in all directions (omni-directional) and laying the fibers in one direction would soon result in a failure.

New reinforcing fibers and resins are constantly being developed. Laminates made from these new products must be tested to find the actual flexural strength.

WOOD

Small boats were usually built of wood until the decade of 1950 and volumes have been written describing the best woods and construction techniques. The contribution of this book is to briefly note the recent developments which have made huge improvements in wood boatbuilding.

Just as the micro chip has revolutionized electronics products, the epoxy saturation of wood has completely changed wood boatbuilding. The Gougeon Brothers of Bay City, Michigan, USA were probably the first to develop the Wood Epoxy Saturation Technique (WEST SYSTEM - a trademark) and they deserve a great deal of credit for advancing wood construction of all types. Their textbook and instruction manuals are strongly recommended for anyone building a wood boat. Their methods can be used with all types of construction; glued veneers (cold molded), carvel, lapstrake or strip planked.

The biggest problem with wood boats is keeping water away from the wood and fastenings. Water soakage causes wood deterioration and rot, severely limiting the life of a hull if it is kept in the water all year. This problem is greatly reduced if the new wood is first saturated with a thinned epoxy resin, before being built into the hull. This resin closes the wood grain and prevents water migration. The wood planks can be glued to each other and to the framing with thickened epoxy glue.

The weight of various woods depends on where it was grown, the species and the moisture content. Spruce can be 26 lbs per cubic foot (416 kg/m^3) while white oak can be 52 lbs per cubic foot (833 kg/m^3). Fir plywood and mahogany usually average 36 lbs per cubic foot (577 kg/m^3).

The best cut of lumber for boatbuilding and fine cabinetwork is "quarter sawn". This is done by cutting the log in four equal pieces and then along a radius, as you would cut a pie. In this manner, the grain is identical in each piece and the plank will not warp as it dries. (Figure 6-11) There is a large amount of waste in cutting a log "quarter sawn" but this is the price we have to pay for top quality. Hopefully, three trees will be planted for each one cut.

Photo 8

Wood boat construction showing knees at the top which connect deck beams to the steam bent frames. The ballast keel bolts are shown on the centerline at the floor timbers. A stainless steel tie rod is just to port of the mast step. This rod stops the deck from flexing. Note the mast step girders projecting over five floor timbers.

Since there are variations in density, grain, knots, checks and voids, wood is not a homogeneous material. Technically, wood should not comply with the formulas for the loading of a beam that have been used for calculating required thickness. In practice, they can be used with a reasonable factor of safety. The hull bottom thickness for wood hulls is shown in Figure 6-8, using a factor of safety of five. Bending tests have shown the outer fibers of wood start cracking at 1600 psi (11024 kPa) and this is the strength used for calculations. Keels on wood boats should be four times the planking thickness, as a minimum. Sailboat keels are usually tapered to meet the ballast thickness. Figure 6-9 shows some examples of wood bottom framing.

FERRO - CEMENT

Boats have been built of ferro-cement for many years and their durability has been well proven. The primary advantage of this material is the low cost and the availability of cement and steel mesh (hardware cloth) in remote areas. These hulls do require a large amount of labor hours and are favored in areas of low labor cost. This factor makes ferro-cement hulls too expensive in highly industrialized nations with high labor rates, except for the owner who builds his own boat.

Most cement is porous and it is vital to seal the surfaces. If water moisture is allowed to reach the steel mesh reinforcing, rust will begin and expansion of the rust will crack the cement from the inside (spalling). This is prevented by sealing the cement with epoxy resin and then using polyurethane paint.

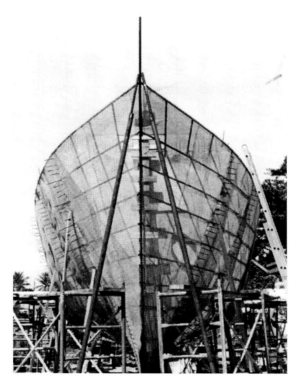

Photo 9

Ferro Cement prefabricated bulkheads are set vertically and faired with steel rods. Prefabricated Ferro Cement longitudinals are then installed before placing the wire mesh.

Photo 11

The deck of a Ferro Cement hull under construction. Note the longitudinal rods on top of the bulkheads. All hatch framing and mast partners are installed at this stage. The rods protruding up from the top edge of the bulkheads will be bent flat and wired to the wire mesh for the deck.

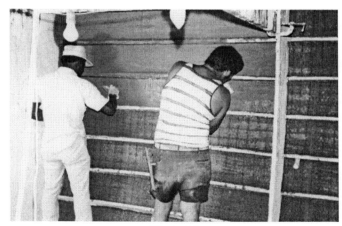

Photo 10

Plasterers are applying cement on the inside of the wire mesh between a bulkhead (left) and a web frame (right). This is a typical construction of a Ferro Cement hull.

The completed ferro-cement structure consists of steel rods and mesh bent around the edges of bulkheads and tightly wired together so the average total thickness of rods and mesh is about one-third the total finished thickness of the hull. The total will weigh about 165 pounds per cubic foot (2643 kg/m³), of which twenty percent is steel rods and mesh. Tests on ferro-cement panels have shown cracking of the material at 1600 psi (11024 kPa) and a factor of safety of five is used. Figures 6-8 and 6-10 show the sample scantlings.

Usually the transverse (web) frames consist of ferro-cement bulkheads with the steel reinforcing tied to the hull at the edges of the bulkheads. See photos 9-11. Longitudinal ferro-cement framing is installed between bulkheads in a similar manner.

The use of beam formulas may be questioned with this material but in actual practice, the results prove to be realistic and durable. Quality control is essential in ferro-cement hull construction to insure the cement is pushed into all the voids in the mesh. This will insure there are no air pockets and insure there is at least a quarter of an inch (6.4 mm) of cement over all the mesh and rods. The entire hull should be cemented in one day.

SUMMARY

This chapter has shown the procedure for calculating hull thickness and stiffener size, which may be used for any material. All composites of plastic and new materials must be tested to insure the correct value for Yield Strength and Flexural Strength.

The technical detail and calculations are necessary as these are the criteria by which the thickness and shape are determined. There is not one best boat material as the choice depends on the objectives of the owner for the specific vessel and the resources that are available.

HULL BOTTOM DESIGN PRESSURE IN psi/kPa								
LWL Ft/m	Weight lb/kg	BOAT SPEED IN KNOTS/KM PER HOUR						
		10/18.5	15/27.8	20/37.1	30/55.6	35/64.9	40/74.2	50/92.7
20 6.1	7,050	3.3	5.2	7.8	15.3	20.1	25.8	39.3
	3,200	22.75	35.8	53.8	105.5	139	178	271
30 9.15	21,100	4.1	6	8.6	16.1	20.9	26.6	40.1
	9,579	28.2	41.3	59.2	111	144	183.5	276
40 12.2	39,000	4.8	6.7	9.3	16.8	21.6	27.3	40.8
	17,706	33.1	46.1	64	115.8	149	188	280.5
50 15.25	64,000	5.5	7.4	10	17.5	22.3	28	41.5
	29,056	37.9	51	68.9	120.5	153.5	193	286
75 22.9	173,000	7.3	9.2	11.8	19.3	24.1	29.8	43.3
	78,542	50.3	63.4	81.4	133	166	205	298
100 30.5	320,000	8.9	10.8	13.4	20.9	25.7	31.4	44.9
	145,280	61.4	74.4	92.2	144	177	216	309
120 36.6	480,000	10.2	12.1	14.7	22.2	27	32.7	46.2
	217,920	70.4	83.4	101.3	153	186	225	318

Figure 6-1

Local loads are additional. Use only for hulls less than 120 ft (36.6 m) LWL. Hullside design pressure is 75% of this chart. Hull framing is 50% design pressure of this chart.

P = .015 (V^2) + .2 $(Disp^{.33})$ + .04 LWL (English units) where P is pounds per square inch (psi), V is in knots, LWL is waterline length in feet, Displacement is in cubic feet.

P = .03 (V^2) + .25 $(Disp^{.33})$ + 1.3 LWL (SI units) where P is kilo Pascals (kPa), V is in km per hour, LWL is waterline length in meters (m), Displacement is kilograms (kg).

LWL Ft/m Weight lb/kg	Frame Spacing in/mm	ALUMINUM HULL BOTTOM THICKNESS BOAT SPEED IN KNOTS/KM PER HOUR						
		10/18.5	15/27.8	20/37.1	30/55.6	35/64.9	40/74.2	50/92.7
20/6.1 7050 3200	20/508	.20/5.1	0.24/6.1	.30/7.6	.42/10.7	.44/11.2	.54/13.7	.66/16.8
	30/762	.30/7.6	.36/9.2	.44/11.2	.62/16	.71/18	.80/20.4	1.0/25.4
30/9.15 21100 5979	20/508	.22/5.6	.26/6.6	.31/7.9	.43/11	.48/12.2	.55/14	.67/17
	30/762	.32/8.1	.39/10	.47/12	.64/16	.73/18.6	.82/21	1.0/25.4
40/12.2 3900 17706	20/508	.23/5.8	.28/7.1	.32/8	.44/11.2	.49/12.5	.55/14	.68/17.3
	30/762	.35/8.9	.41/10	.48/12.2	.65/16.5	.74/18.8	.83/21	1.01/26
50/15.2 64000 29056	20/508	.25/6.4	.29/7.4	.34/8.6	.45/11.5	.50/12.7	.56/14.2	.69/17.5
	30/762	.37/9.4	.43/11	.50/12.7	.66/16.8	.75/19	.84/21.4	1.02/26
75/22.9 173000 78542	20/508	.29/7.4	.32/8.1	.36/9.2	.46/11.7	.52/13.2	.58/14.7	.70/17.8
	30/762	.43/11	.48/12.2	.54/13.7	.70/17.8	.78/20	.86/22	1.04/26.4
100/30.5 320000 145280	20/508	.34/8.6	.35/8.9	.39/10	.48/12.2	.54/13.7	.59/15	.72/18.3
	30/762	.51/13	.52/13.2	.58/14.7	.73/18.6	.80/20.4	.89/22.6	1.10/28

Figure 6-2

Yield strength assumed at 18,000 psi (124,020 kPa). Different spacing and additional cargo loads require calculation. Thickness is in inches/mm.

Web LWL Ft/m Longitudinal	ALUMINUM HULL BOTTOM FRAMING BOAT SPEED IN KNOTS/KM PER HOUR			
	10/18.5	20/37.1	30/55.6	40/74.2
Web 20/6.1	2.6/42.6 3x3x.25 76x76x6	4.9/80.4 5x3x.25 127x76x6	11/181 8x4x.25 200x102x6	14.3/234 8x6x.25 200x152x6
Longitudinal	2.6/42.6 3x3x.25 76x76x6	3.7/60.6 4x3x.25 102x76x6	6.9/113.2 6x3.5x.25 152x89x6	11/181 8x4x.25 200x102x6
Web 30/9.15	3.7/60.6 4x3x.25 102x76x6	6.9/113.2 6x3.5x.25 152x89x6	14.3/234 8x6x.25 200x152x6	22.6/370 10x3.5x.50 254x89x13
Longitudinal	2.6/42.6 3x3x.25 76x76x6	3.7/60.6 4x3x.25 102x76x6	6.9/113.2 6x3.5x.25 152x89x6	12.7/208 8x5x.25 200x127x6
Web 40/12.2	6/98.5 6x3.5x.25 152x89x6	11/181 8x4x.25 200x102x6	20.3/333 10x4x.375 254x102x9.5	30/492 13x5x.375 330x127x9.5
Longitudinal	2.6/42.6 3x3x.25 76x76x6	4.9/80.4 5x3x.25 127x76x6	11/181 8x4x.25 200x102x6	12.7/208 8x5x.25 200x127x6
Web 50/15.25	11/181 8x4x.25 200x102x6	14.3/234 8x6x.25 200x152x6	25/410 11x5x.375 280x27x9.5	47.3/775 16x8x.375 406x200x9.5
Longitudinal	2.6/42.6 3x3x.25 76x76x6	4.9/80.4 5x3x.25 127x76x6	11/181 8x4x.25 200x102x6	14.3/234 8x6x.25 200x152x6
Web 75/22.9	14.3/234 8x6x.25 200x152x6	22.6/370 10x3.5x.50 254x89x13	47.3/775 16x8x.375 406x200x9.5	58.8/965 18x4x.625 457x102x16
Longitudinal	3.7/60.6 4x3x.25 102x76x6	6.9/113.2 6x3.5x.25 152x89x6	11/181 8x4x.25 200x102x6	14.3/234 8x6x.25 200x152x6
Web 100/30.5	20.3/333 10x4x.375 254x102x9.5	30/492 13x5x.375 330x127x9.5	47.3/775 16x8x.375 406x200x9.5	74.8/1230 18x4x.625 457x102x16
Longitudinal	3.7/60.6 4x3x.25 102x76x6	6.9/113.2 6x3.5x.25 152x89x6	11/181 8x4x.25 200x102x6	14.3/234 8x6x.25 200x152x6

Figure 6-3

Figure 6-3 above shows section modulus (in³ & cm³) and sizes of angle frames (inches & mm) for transverse (web) frames spaced 96 inches (2440 mm) and longitudinals spaced 20 inches (508 mm). Material yield stress assumed at 18,000 psi (124,020 kPa). Other spacing must be calculated.

LWL Ft/m Weight lb/kg	Frame Spacing in/mm	HULL BOTTOM THICKNESS FOR STEEL HULLS BOAT SPEED IN KNOTS/KM PER HOUR						
		10/18.5	15/27.8	20/37.1	30/55.6	35/64.9	40/74.2	50/92.7
20/6.1 7050 3200	20/508	.15/3.8	.19/4.8	.23/5.8	.32/8.1	.37/9.4	.41/10.5	.51/13
	30/762	.23/5.8	.28/7.1	.34/8.6	.48/12.2	.55/14	.62/15.8	.77/19.6
30/9.15 21100 9579	20/508	.16/4.1	.20/5.1	.24/6.1	.33/8.4	.37/9.4	.42/10.7	.52/13.2
	30/762	.25/6.4	.30/7.6	.36/9.2	.50/12.7	.56/14.3	.63/16	.78/20
40/12.2 39000 17706	20/508	.18/4.6	.21/5.3	.25/6.4	.34/8.6	.38/9.7	.43/11	.53/13.5
	30/762	.27/6.9	.32/8.1	.37/9.4	.50/12.7	.57/14.5	.64/16.3	.79/20
50/15.25 64000 29056	20/508	.19/4.8	.22/5.6	.26/6.6	.35/8.9	.39/9.9	.44/11.2	.53/13.5
	30/762	.29/7.4	.33/8.4	.39/9.9	.51/13	.58/14.8	.65/16.5	.79/20
75/22.9 173000 78542	20/508	.22/5.6	.25/6.4	.27/6.9	.36/9.2	.40/10.2	.45/11.4	.54/13.7
	30/762	.33/8.4	.37/9.4	.42/10.7	.54/13.7	.60/15.3	.67/17	.81/20.6
100/30.5 320000 145280	20/508	.25/6.4	.27/6.9	.30/7.6	.37/9.4	.42/10.7	.46/11.7	.55/14
	30/762	.37/9.4	.40/10.2	.45/11.5	.56/14.2	.62/15.8	.69/17.5	.82/20.9

Figure 6-4

This table assumes a yield strength of 30,000 psi (206,700 kPa). Different spacing and additional loads require calculation. Thickness is in inches/mm.

Web LWL Ft/m Longitudinal	STEEL HULL BOTTOM FRAMING BOAT SPEED IN KNOTS/KM PER HOUR			
	10/18.5	20/37.1	30/55.6	40/74.2
Web 20/6.1	1.5/24.6 2.5x2x.25 64x51x6	2.6/42.6 3x3x.25 76x76x6	6.9/113.2 6x3.5x.25 152x89x6	11/181 8x4x.25 200x102x6
Longitudinal	1.5/24.6 2.5x2x.25 64x51x6	2.6/42.6 3x3x.25 76x76x6	4.9/80.4 5x3x.25 127x76x6	6.9/113.2 6x3.5x.25 152x89x6
Web 30/9.15	2.6/42.6 3x3x.25 76x76x6	4.9/80.4 5x3x.25 127x76x6	11/181 8x4x.25 200x102x6	12.7/208 8x5x.25 200x127x6
Longitudinal	1.5/24.6 2.5x2x.25 64x51x6	2.6/42.6 3x3x.25 76x76x6	4.9/80.4 5x3x.25 127x76x6	6.9/113.2 6x3.5x.25 152x89x6
Web 40/12.2	3.7/60.6 4x3x.25 102x76x6	6.9/113.2 6x3.5x.25 152x89x6	11/181 8x4x.25 200x102x6	20.3/333 10x4x.375 254x102x9.5
Longitudinal	1.5/24.6 2.5x2x.25 64x51x6	2.6/42.6 3x3x.25 76x76x6	4.9/80.4 5x3x.25 127x76x6	11/181 8x4x.25 200x102x6
Web 50/15.25	4.9/80.4 5x3x.25 127x76x6	11/181 8x4x.25 200x102x6	15.7/258 7x4x.50 178x102x13	35.4/580 13x4x.61 330x102x16
Longitudinal	1.5/24.6 2.5x2x.25 64x51x6	2.6/42.6 3x3x.25 76x76x6	4.9/80.4 5x3x.25 127x76x6	11/181 8x4x.25 200x102x6
Web 75/22.9	11/181 8x4x.25 200x102x6	12.7/208 8x5x.25 200x127x6	22.6/370 10x3.5x.50 254x89x13	35.4/580 13x4x.61 330x102x16
Longitudinal	2.6/42.6 3x3x.25 76x76x6	3.7/60.6 4x3x.25 102x76x6	6.9/113.2 6x3.5x.25 152x89x6	11/181 8x4x.25 200x102x6
Web 100/30.5	12.7/208 8x5x.25 200x127x6	20.3/333 10x4x.375 254x102x9.5	35.4/580 13x4x.61 330x102x16	47.3/775 16x8x.375 406x200x9.5
Longitudinal	2.6/42.6 3x3x.25 76x76x6	3.7/60.6 4x3x.25 102x76x6	6.9/113.2 6x3.5x.25 152x89x6	11/181 8x4x.25 200x102x6

Figure 6-5 above shows section modulus (in³ & cm³) and sizes of angle frames (inches & mm) for transverse (web) frames spaced 96 inches (2440 mm) and longitudinals spaced 20 inches (508 mm). Material yield stress assumed at 30,000 psi (206,700 kPa). Other spacing must be calculated.

LWL Ft/m Weight lb/kg	Frame Spacing in/mm	AVERAGE GLASS FIBER LAMINATES BOAT SPEED IN KNOTS/KM PER HOUR				
		10/18.5	20/37.1	30/55.6	40/74.2	50/92.7
20/6.1 7050 3200	20/508	.32/8.2	.42/10.7	.53/13.5	.63/16	.74/18.8
	30/762	.47/12	.63/16	.79/20	.94/24	1.10/28
30/9.15 21100 9579	20/508	.34/8.6	.44/11.2	.54/13.7	.64/16.3	.74/18.8
	30/762	.51/13	.65/16.5	.80/20.4	.95/24.2	1.12/29
40/12.2 39000 17706	20/508	.36/9.2	.45/11.4	.54/13.7	.64/16.3	.75/19
	30/762	.54/14	.67/17	.82/20.8	.96/24.4	1.12/29
50/15.25 64000 29056	20/508	.38/9.7	.46/11.7	.55/14	.65/16.5	.76/19.3
	30/762	.56/14	.69/17.5	.83/21.1	.97/24.7	1.13/29
75/22.9 173000 78542	20/508	.41/10.4	.48/12.2	.57/14.5	.66/16.8	.77/19.6
	30/762	.62/15.8	.73/18.6	.86/22	.99/25.2	1.16/30
100/30.5 320000 145280	20/508	.44/11.2	.51/13	.59/15	.67/17	.79/20
	30/762	.66/16.8	.76/19.3	.88/22.4	1.01/26	1.18/30

Figure 6-6

This table shows the hull bottom thickness in inches (mm). Check local loads on each hull. Flexural strength assumed at 29,000 psi (199,810 kPa). Use FS=2 and double thickness at centerline for 24 in (610 mm). Thickness is in inches/mm.

Web LWL Ft/m Longitudinal	GLASS FIBER HULL BOTTOM FRAMING BOAT SPEED IN KNOTS/KM PER HOUR			
	10/18.5	20/37.1	30/55.6	40/74.2
Web 20/6.1	6.7/110 5x1 127x25.4	12.7/208 7x1 178x25.4	17/279 8x1 204x25.4	20/328 9x1 229x25.4
Longitudinal	6.7/110 5x1 127x25.4	12.7/208 7x1 178x25.4	17/279 8x1 204x25.4	20/328 9x1 229x25.4
Web 30/9.15	6.7/110 5x1 127x25.4	12.7/208 7x1 178x25.4	17/279 8x1 204x25.4	32/525 10x1 254x25.4
Longitudinal	6.7/110 5x1 127x25.4	12.7/208 7x1 178x25.4	17/279 8x1 204x25.4	20/328 9x1 229x25.4
Web 40/12.2	9/148 6x1 152x25.4	17/279 8x1 204x25.4	32/525 10x1 254x25.4	37/606 12x1 305x25.4
Longitudinal	6.7/110 5x1 127x25.4	12.7/208 7x1 178x25.4	17/279 8x1 204x25.4	20/328 9x1 229x25.4
Web 50/15.25	12.7/208 7x1 178x25.4	20/328 9x1 229x25.4	37/606 12x1 305x25.4	50/820 14x1 356x25.4
Longitudinal	9/148 6x1 152x25.4	12.7/208 7x1 178x25.4	17/279 8x1 204x25.4	20/328 9x1 229x25.4
Web 75/22.9	20/328 9x1 229x25.4	37/606 12x1 305x25.4	50/820 14x1 356x25.4	64/1050 16x1 406x25.4
Longitudinal	9/148 6x1 152x25.4	12.7/208 7x1 178x25.4	17/279 8x1 204x25.4	32/525 10x1 254x25.4
Web 100/30.5	32/525 10x1 254x25.4	37/606 12x1 305x25.4	64/1050 16x1 406x25.4	102/1675 20x1 508x25.4
Longitudinal	12.7/208 7x1 178x25.4	17/279 8x1 204x25.4	32/525 10x1 254x25.4	37/606 12x1 305x25.4

Figure 6-7 above shows section modulus (in³ & cm³) and sizes of flat bar frames (inches & mm) for transverse (web) frames spaced 96 inches (2440 mm) and longitudinals spaced 20 inches (508 mm). Glass fiber laminate bending stress assumed at 29,000 psi (200,000 kPa). Use FS=2.0.

LWL Ft/m Weight lb/kg	Frame Spacing in/cm	WOOD & FERRO CEMENT BOAT SPEED IN KNOTS/KM PER HOUR			
		10/18.5	15/27.8	20/37.1	30/55.6
20/6.1 7050/3200	10 25.4	.72 1.9	.88 2.3	1.1 2.8	1.55 4
30/9.15 21100/9579	10 25.4	.80 2	.966 2.5	1.16 3	1.59 4.1
40/12.2 39000/17706	12 30.5	1.04 2.7	1.23 3.1	1.45 3.7	1.94 5
50/15.25 64000/29056	15 38	1.4 3.6	1.62 4.1	1.88 4.8	2.50 6.4
75/22.9 173000/78542	18 46	1.93 5	2.16 5.5	2.44 6.2	3.12 8
100/30.5 320000/145280	20 50.8	2.36 6	2.60 6.4	2.90 7.4	3.62 9.2

Figure 6-8

This table shows the hull bottom thickness in inches (cm). Commercial vessels require 30% additional thickness. Material cracking begins at 1600 psi (11024 kPa). Use factor of safety of 5.0. If wood veneers and epoxy glues are used, the total thickness can be 80% of this table.

LWL Ft/m Weight lb/kg	WOOD HULL BOTTOM FRAMING BOAT SPEED IN KNOTS/KM PER HOUR	
	10/18.5	20/37.1
20/6.1 7050 3200	2.7 in^3/44 cm^3 1x3 in 2.54x7.62 cm spaced 10 in/25.4 cm	5.4 in^3/89 cm^3 1.5x3 in 3.8 x 7.62 cm spaced 10 in/25.4 cm
30/9.15 21100 9579	5.4 in^3/89 cm^3 1.5x3 in 3.8 x 7.62 cm spaced 10 in/25.4 cm	11 in^3/180cm^3 2x4 in 5.1 x 10.2 cm spaced 10 in/30.5 cm
40/12.2 39000 17706	11 in^3/180cm^3 2x4 in 5.1 x 10.2 cm spaced 12 in/30.5 cm	16.3 in^3/267 cm^3 3x4 in 7.62x10.2 cm spaced 12 in/38 cm
50/15.25 64000 29056	16.3 in^3/267 cm^3 3x4 in 7.62x10.2 cm spaced 15 in/38 cm	34 in^3/267 cm^3 2x7 in 5.1x17.8 cm spaced 15 in/46cm
75/22.9 173000 78542	34 in^3/267 cm^3 2x7 in 5.1x17.8 cm spaced 18 in/46cm	54 in^3/885 cm^3 2x8 in 5.1x20.4 cm spaced 18 in/50.8 cm
100/30.5 320000 145280	54 in^3/885 cm^3 2x8 in 5.1x20.4 cm spaced 20 in/50.8 cm	76 in3/1247 cm3 4x8 in 10.2x20.4 cm spaced 20 in/50.8 cm

Figure 6-9

A few examples of section modulus and sizes of transverse frames spaced as shown with the largest dimension set vertically in the hull. Local loads require additional framing. Wood begins cracking (Average fiber stress) at 1600 psi (11,024 kPa).

LWL Ft/m Weight lb/kg	Longitudinal Spacing in/cm	FERRO CEMENT HULL BOTTOM FRAMING BOAT SPEED IN KNOTS/KM PER HOUR	
		10/18.5	20/37.1
20/6.1 7050/3200	Web	25 in³/410 cm³ 9x1/23x2.54	55 in³/900 cm³ 14x1/36x2.54
	Longitudinal 10/25.4	9 in³/147.5 cm³ 5x1/12.7x2.54	20 in³/328 cm³ 8x1/20.4x2.54
30/9.15	Web	37 in³/606 cm³ 12x1/30.5x2.54	80 in³/1310 cm³ 18x1/45.8x2.54
21100/9579	Longitudinal 10/25.4	12.3 in³/202 cm³ 6x1/15.3x2.54	20 in³/328 cm³ 8x1/20.4x2.54
40/12.2	Web	60 in³/984 cm³ 10x2/25.4x5.1	115 in³/1890 cm³ 15x2/38x5.1
39000/17706	Longitudinal 12/30.5	14 in³/230 cm³ 7x1/17.8x2.54	30 in³/492 cm³ 10x1/25.4x2.54
50/15.25	Web	102 in³/1670 cm³ 20x1/50.8x2.54	172 in³/2820 cm³ 18x2/45.8x5.1
64000/29056	Longitudinal 15/38	20 in³/328 cm³ 8x1/20.4x2.54	37 in³/606 cm³ 12x1/30.5x2.54
75/22.9	Web	150 in³/2460 cm³ 17x2/43.2x5.1	240 in³/3933 cm³ 26x2/66x5.1
173000/78542	Longitudinal 18/46	37 in³/606 cm³ 12x1/30.5x2.54	55 in³/900 cm³ 14x1/35.6x2.54
100/30.5	Web	244 in³/3670 cm³ 21x2/53.4x5.1	427 in³/7000 cm³ 30x2/76.2x5.1
320000/145280	Longitudinal 20/50.8	55 in³/900 cm³ 14x1/35.6x2.54	65 in³/1066 cm³ 12x1.5/30.5x3.81

Figure 6-10

A few examples of section modulus and sizes of flat bar transverse (web) frames spaced 96 inches (244 cm) and longitudinals spaced as shown. Material begins cracking at 1,600 psi (11,024 kPa). The largest dimension is vertical.

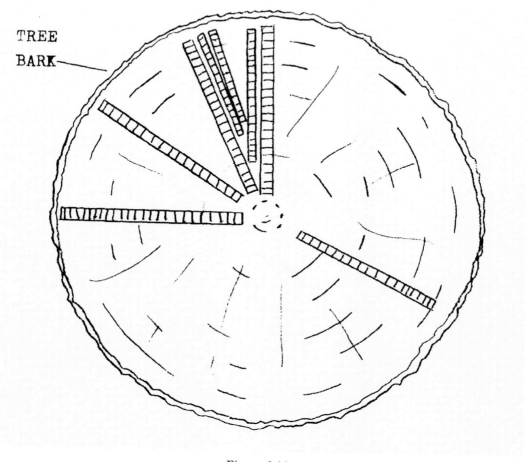

TREE
BARK

Figure 6-11

Quarter Sawn Lumber
The log is cut on a radius so the wood grain is identical in each plank.

CHAPTER SEVEN

THE UNSINKABLE BOAT

Boat owners are always concerned with safety as shown by their preference for two engines in a powerboat, to insure one is running for a safe return to port. They also would enjoy the thought their boat is unsinkable. This chapter details the use of foam flotation material to accomplish that objective.

In addition to foam flotation, it is necessary to keep any flooding from spreading from the point of origin. This is accomplished by making many watertight compartments. Bulkheads are made watertight to the hull and the cabin sole (floor) is watertight on all edges. Hull stiffeners are installed with a height to make a watertight seal with the cabin sole and the volume between stiffeners is filled with foam, wherever it would not interfere with tanks, valves and piping. Watertight hatches are used both in the bulkheads and in the cabin sole.

FLOTATION TYPE AND PLACEMENT

Flotation may be of plastic foam, cork, encapsulated balsa wood or other lightweight, non-porous material. Half of this material must be located on the hull sides in unballasted hulls to prevent the boat floating upside down when flooded.

In some boats, there is not sufficient space available to locate all the required amount of flotation in the bottom or in the hull sides. Additional foam (or other) may be secured inside a flotation ring, built of the hull material and located outboard of the sheer on both sides. The size of this flotation ring is determined by the volume of foam to be installed there.

CALCULATING THE VOLUME OF FLOTATION MATERIAL

The amount of flotation material required varies widely in different hulls, depending on the hull material, amount of ballast, number of engines, generators and other heavy equipment. For these reasons, calculations must be made for each hull. Experience shows unballasted hulls may require fifty percent of the displacement volume for flotation, while steel hulls with ballast may require seventy percent.

Calculation for the amount of flotation material must be carefully accomplished and each item in the boat has to be listed with its weight and volume. The weight list of Figure 5-1 is used to assist in the procedure. Some minor assumptions are made in investigating each item. For example, the weight of an engine is assumed to be all steel and the weight of a berth or cabinet is assumed to be all wood. The weights of galley appliances, sinks, pots and food must be considered separately rather than grouping them together with the cabinets, counters and drawers. An aluminum mast is separated from the steel tangs, fittings and wire rigging.

The flotation calculations are based on Archimedes law of flotation which states that a floating body displaces its own weight of water. In other words, each cubic foot (m^3) of every submerged item is buoyed by one cubic foot (m^3) of sea water.

The densities of a few boat materials are:

Aluminum	165 lbs/ft^3	2643 kg/m^3
Bronze	480 to 520	7689 kg/m^3
Canned Food (12oz)	50 lbs/ft^3	801 kg/m^3
Sodas in 12oz		
aluminum cans	42 lbs/ft^3	673 kg/m^3
Ferro-Cement	165 lbs/ft^3	2643 kg/m^3
Copper 550 lbs/ft^3	8810 kg/m^3	
Glass Fiber	96 lbs/ft^3	535 kg/m^3
Gasoline	46 lbs/ft^3	737 kg/m^3
Diesel Fuel	53 lbs/ft^3	849 kg/m^3
Lead	700 lbs/ft^3	11213 kg/m^3
Oak	52 lbs/ft^3	833 kg/m^3
Fir Plywood	36 lbs/ft^3	577 kg/m^3

Steel	490 lbs/ft³	7849 kg/m³
Window glass	160 lbs/ft³	2563 kg/m³
Fresh water	62.4 lbs/ft³	1000 kg/m³
Sea Water	64 lbs/ft³	1025 kg/m³

The weight of each item in the boat is divided by its density to find the volume in cuft (m³). The total of all the volumes is subtracted from the displacement volume, giving the required volume of flotation material.

For example, an engine that weighs 875 pounds (397 kg) is divided by the density of steel, above, to find its volume, 875 / 490 = 1.79 cuft (.05 m³). If a wood berth weighs 120 pounds (54.4 kg), the weight is divided by the wood density (36lb/ft³ - 577 kg/m³) to get its volume of 3.33 ft³ (.094 m³). The total weight of the particular flotation material must be added to the total displacement of the boat before determining the volume required. A sample calculation for flotation is provided in Figure 7 - 1.

SUMMARY

This chapter has noted boat safety can be greatly improved if the boat is made unsinkable. Different types of flotation material were listed and the method is explained for calculation of required flotation volume. Small spaces outboard of lockers and drawers may seem insignificant but their volume quickly accumulates to provide added security.

FLOATATION REQUIREMENTS FOR A 37 FT LWL/11.3 GLASS FIBER POWERBOAT						
ITEM	WEIGHT		DENSITY		VOLUME	
	LB	KG	LB/FT³	KG/M³	FT³	M³
Hull/framing	6,400	2,903	100	1,602	64	1.81
Deck/deck house	3,000	1,362	100	1,602	30	0.85
Deck hardware	900	408	490	7,849	1.8	0.05
Steering/ rudder	500	227	490	7,849	1	0.03
Engines/ batteries	5,850	2,654	490	7,849	11.9	0.34
Genset/cb panel	1,150	522	490	7,849	2.4	0.07
Prop/shaft/struts	760	344	490	7,849	1.6	0.04
Exhaust/thru hull	1,000	454	490	7,849	2	0.06
Plumbing/electrical	1,500	681	490	7,849	3.1	0.09
2 Alum. tanks	500	227	165	2,643	3	0.09
Fwd berth/sole	300	136	40	641	7.5	0.21
Stateroom/sole	450	204	40	641	11.3	0.32
Paint/trim	640	290	100	1,602	6.4	0.18
Crew/gear	1,800	816	100	1,602	18	0.51
Head/bulkheads	700	318	100	1,602	7	0.2
Dinning table/seats	350	159	40	641	8.7	0.25
Galley cabinets/sole	300	136	40	641	7.5	0.21
Galley appliances	300	136	490	7,849	0.6	0.02
Galley stores	400	181	50	801	8	0.23
Total Volume of Boat Material					195.8	5.55
Foam Flotation	1,000	454	4.2	67.3	238.6	6.76
DISPLACEMENT	27,800	12,621	64	1,025	434.4	12.3

Figure 7-1

This is an example of an unballasted glass fiber powerboat. 1000 lbs (454 kg) of foam is used as floatation. Fuel and water are not included as they are almost neutral in the calculation. The total volume of material in the boat is subtracted from the displacement volume to get the required amount of foam.

CHAPTER EIGHT

SPEED, THE REDUCTION GEAR AND PROPELLERS

Every boat owner wants to know how to determine the speed of his boat and the correct propeller size. This chapter will answer those questions and will show a new formula for speeds of fast hulls. Each of these factors is determined by the designer before the hull lines are drawn, as speed influences the shape of the hull and the overall operating characteristics of any type of vessel.

THE SPEED - LENGTH RATIO

One of the most important design indicators is speed - length ratio as it is used to judge the relative speed of any hull. It defines the relationship between slow speed (displacement speed), moderate speed and fast hulls. The basis for this ratio comes from the speed of an ocean wave that has been measured as 1.34 multiplied by the square root of the length between wave crests: (V is velocity)

V (kt) = 1.34 $L^{.5}$ (ft) or V (km/hr) = 4.49 $L^{.5}$ (m) The speed - length ratio is $V/LWL^{.5}$ (waterline length).

To explain this further, consider the wave formed at the bow and at the stern of a boat moving through the water. As the speed is slowly increased, these waves become one, with the crests at the bow and at the stern. At a speed - length ratio of 1.34 (4.49 metric), the hull has settled into the trough of this wave and without sufficient power to climb the crest at the bow, the hull is said to be moving at displacement speed. Displacement speed hulls have a speed - length ratio of less than 1.34 (4.49 metric). Moderate speed boats have a speed - length ratio between 1.34 and 3.0 (4.49 to 10 metric). Faster boats are called planing hulls and have a large total horsepower that allows them to push over the bow wave (V/LWL$^{.5}$ is over 3.0 (10 metric).

For example, a sailboat with a 25 foot (7.6 m) waterline length and moving at five knots (9.25km/hr) has a speed - length ratio of 1.0 (3.35 metric). The same relative speed can be found on a 900 foot (274.5 m) waterline length aircraft carrier with a speed of 30 knots (55.5km/hr). Both hulls have a speed - length ratio of 1.0 (3.35 metric) and both hulls are called displacement speed vessels. This relationship of length and speed influences most aspects of hull design. Profit making cargo vessels are displacement hulls and move at speed - length ratios of about 0.8 (2.68 metric), which is in their region of the most economical speed.

A NEW BOAT SPEED FORMULA

Many people have worked on ways to determine boat speed and methods have been developed that are very accurate. Most of these procedures are available on proprietary computer programs. In an attempt to simplify the procedure and to avoid the variable coefficients of other methods, I have compiled the results of many boat tests over a period of thirty years. The data were plotted and the following formula was developed:

$$V^2 \text{ (KT) x LB / HP} = 28750 \text{ or } V^2 \text{ (km/hr) x kg / HP} = 44000$$

This formula is used only when the LB/HP ratio is less than 75 (34 kg/HP). The manufacturer's advertised engine horsepower is used in the equation. On slower boats, the waterline length becomes an important factor which can also be observed from boat tests. The data for both slow and fast hulls is presented in Figure 8-1.

The data from many manufacturer's boat tests indicate the tests are not properly performed or the boats had a poor hull form. Some of the causes of poor boat tests are as follows:

    a. The measured mile may not be accurate.

    b. An average of three runs on the measured mile was not taken. This elimi-
nates the effects of temporary winds, currents and human error.

    c. The time is not noted at the exact end of the mile.

    d. The "radar" gun may not be calibrated.

    e. Barnacles are on the hull bottom and propeller.

    f. The boat is not in level trim.

    g. The propeller may be the wrong size.

    h. The engine may not have sufficient air for proper fuel combustion.

    i. The fuel may be contaminated with dirt or water.

    j. The spark plugs are fouled (gasoline).

BOATS WITH UNUSUAL SPEEDS

Higher than normal speeds are made by some boats outside the usual formulas for speed prediction. Air cushion vehicles (hovercraft) use a very high horsepower engine to physically lift the hull off the surface and then propel it forward. They are more a form of aircraft engineering than boat, as the hull is airborne. Hydrofoils act like boats when the hull is in the water but with the very expensive addition of foils to get the hull out of the water when there is fast forward motion. Hydrofoils have proven very effective as passenger ferries in calm, protected, waters but some have not stayed up on the foils in ocean conditions.

Unballasted, very light weight, racing sailboats are exceptions to the slow, displacement speeds of cruising sailboats, either monohull or multihull. These racing sailboats attain unusually high speeds only when they are not sailing to windward. Then only for a short period of time when the wind is aft of the beam and of sufficient strength. Capsizes of these hulls are common and expected when racing. Ballasted sailboats in long ocean waves can achieve higher than normal speeds for a short period of time by traveling with the crest of a wave (surfing) when the wind and waves are from the same direction.

THE REDUCTION GEAR AND
MINIMUM PROPELLER DIAMETER

After the speed formula is used with the desired speed to determine the required horsepower, the reduction gear is selected. The reduction gear on the engine is in the same housing as the reverse gear and serves the purpose of lowering the propeller RPM (revolutions per minute) from the engine RPM to allow the correct diameter propeller. A lower propeller RPM requires a larger diameter propeller with the same engine horsepower if the maximum engine RPM is to be maintained at wide open throttle. A heavy hull requires a larger diameter propeller than a light weight, fast hull of the same length. This results from the heavy hull requiring more thrust to propel it.

The efficiency of a propeller depends on a low thrust per square inch of area and larger and heavier hulls require a larger propeller diameter (more area) to keep the pressure on the blades within reasonable limits. The propeller transmits the rotating force of the engine (torque) to thrust. The maximum engine HP and RPM and the maximum propeller RPM, are used in this chapter for propeller selection.

As a starting point, experience with many hulls has shown the minimum propeller diameter may be estimated from the following formula, which is explained on Figure 8-2:

$$D^2 \text{ (in)} = 29 \text{ A (sqft) or } D^2 \text{ (cm)} = 2000 \text{ A (m}^2)$$

Where A is the largest submerged sectional area of the hull. Figure 8-2 shows this formula in tabular form. The table of propeller diameters is then entered with the minimum diameter and the horsepower of one engine. The maximum RPM is selected and divided into the engine's maximum RPM to get the reduction gear ratio; 2:1, 2.5:1, for example. Specify the closest but slightly larger ratio available from the engine manufacturer. Some light weight, fast boats may not use any reduction in RPM, while heavy, slow hulls like tugboats may use 6:1. Sailboats generally use 2:1, 2.5:1 or 3:1 gears.

For example, if we have a thirty three foot (10 m) boat with the largest sectional area of 8.81 sqft (0.815 m^2) and a 150 HP engine, the minimum propeller diameter is 16 in (40.6 cm): D^2 = 29 x 8.81 = 256; D = 16 in. Entering Figure 8-4 we find the maximum RPM for the propeller is 2400, which would require a 1.25:1 gear if the maximum engine RPM is 3000. We also find in the engine catalog the available reduction gear ratios are 1:1, 1.5:1 and 2:1. We should then select a 1.5:1 gear and the propeller RPM would be 2000, maximum. Returning to the propeller diameter chart (Figure 8-4), we find the correct propeller diameter for the 150 HP engine at 2000 RPM at the propeller, is 18 in (45 cm).

PROPELLER DIAMETER & PITCH CHARTS

The correct selection of propeller size and type is a very complex subject worthy of a lifetime of study. The boat owner and designer are thus well advised to consult the propeller manufacturers to ask their recommendations. The local propeller sales and repair shop is usually the starting point in contacting the manufacturers. These specialists publish charts for diameter and pitch determination from which Figure 8-3, *PROPELLER PITCH* and Figure 8-4, *PROPELLER DIAMETER*, have been compiled. The manufacturers have always been very cooperative in helping with any problem and the I thank them for their assistance.

It is normal for the ratio of propeller pitch to diameter to be 0.5 for displacement hulls. This ratio for moderate speed hulls can be from 0.6 to 0.8; and 0.9 to 1.2 for planing hulls. The propeller diameter is determined early in the design stages and definitely before the hull lines are drawn to be certain proper clearances are assured.

PROPELLER LOCATION, ROTATION AND
NUMBER OF BLADES

The propeller location and diameter influence the operating draft of the boat as it normal to have the propeller below the hull bottom. A keel or skeg is necessary to protect the propeller when aground on either single or twin engine hulls. The clearance between the top of the propeller and the hull should be 20% of propeller diameter. The clearance between the rudder and the aft end of the propeller shaft should be twice the length of the propeller hub so the propeller can easily be removed. Consult the propeller manufacturer's catalogs for this data and for propeller weights. The rudder should have a recess on single engine boats so the shaft will clear the rudder on removal. On twin engine boats, the rudder is located off the shaft centerline so the shaft can be removed easily.

There are some patented, high speed propeller installations where the shaft comes aft from the transom rather than under the boat. This reduces the operating draft and the boat speed is increased by about ten percent, as no drag producing projections are under the hull. These are called surface piercing propellers and the system manufacturers should be consulted for each boat.

Usually, the propeller manufacturers will recommend a three blade propeller for boats under 45 feet (13.7 m) and four blades for larger hulls. Sailboats have traditionally used a two bladed propeller to reduce drag while under sail but a three bladed propeller is always more efficient. Many owners will install a three blade propeller when they will be making a long trip under power. There is no substitute for a large blade area on displacement hulls. Any engine develops its maximum horsepower at the maximum rated RPM and the propeller diameter should be large enough to allow this rated RPM but no faster.

When two propellers are installed, one rotates clockwise when seen from astern (right hand) and the other rotates in the opposite direction. This cancels the sideways movement of the stern caused by propeller rotation. By custom, the right hand propeller is placed on the starboard side. Also by custom, a single engine boat has right hand propeller rotation. Everyone then knows the stern will move to port when backing.

The stern moves to port when backing as the bottom propeller blade imparts a stronger force to the water than the upper blades. The right hand propeller is turning counter clockwise when backing and the lower blade is essentially moving from port to starboard. This force on the water produces an equal and opposite reaction on the stern of the boat and the stern moves to port.

This phenomenon probably occurs as the upper blades are operating in a turbulent mixture of air and water and they are not as effective as the lower blades. This movement of the stern also occurs when the single engine boat is going ahead. The stern moves to starboard due to propeller forces but it is not as noticeable as there is much greater forward movement when compared with the slow backing movement. When going ahead, the single engine hull will always require a slight helm to starboard to counteract the stern motion, also to starboard, with a right hand propeller, turning clockwise.

When the engines are ordered, the rotation must be specified as this is determined by the location of the gears in the reverse/reduction gear housing. Also, the builder must know of this rotation.

The rotation of a propeller can be recognized by looking at the blade edge closest to you. If the blade edge farthest away is to the right of the closest edge, it is a right hand propeller and conversely. This method works when looking at either the front or back of the propeller. Two and three bladed propellers are used on cruising sailboats. Three bladed propellers on powerboats under 40 feet (12.2 m). Larger powerboats normally use four bladed propellers as the larger blade area is more efficient.

THE PROPELLER SHAFT

The diameter of the propeller shaft is dependent on the rotating force (torque) applied by the engine and by the resisting force (yield stress in torsion) of the material. Shafts have been made from bronze, steel and stainless steel but most new shafts are made from special alloys of stainless steel that have a high yield stress in torsion. Some manufacturers have made a specialty of propeller shafts and they should be consulted for each hull. The allowable yield stress in torsion for type 304 stainless steel is about 20,000 psi (138 MPa) and about 70,000 psi (482 MPa) for type 630 stainless steel.

Figure 8-5 has been compiled from the following formula for shaft diameter, using a factor of safety (FS) of 3.8 on the yield stress allowed:

d^3 (in) = 321000 x HP x FS / RPM x Yield Stress (psi)
d^3 (mm) = 36 x 10^6 x HP x FS / RPM x Yield Stress (MPa)
d^3 = 321000 (300hp) 3.8 / 1200 RPM (20,000) = 15.2475 and diameter is 2.47 inches. (64 mm), for example.

The propeller shaft will require bearings if the distance between the strut bearing and the engine coupling is too great a distance. The shaft log (stuffing box) is not considered to be a bearing.

PROPELLER SHAFT BEARINGS

The propeller shaft must be supported and not allowed to move from side to side. Excessive movement will ruin the bearings in the reverse/reduction gear housing. The aft shaft bearing is in the propeller shaft strut, which must be rigidly bolted through the hull, using backing plates on the inside. Bearings should not be located within two feet (0.6 m) of the engine coupling.

The following table gives the maximum bearing spacing for shaft diameters of 20,000 psi (138MPa) yield stress:

SHAFT DIAMETER inches or mm	MAXIMUM BEARING SPACING feet or meters
0.75 in (19 mm)	4.0 ft (1.22 m)
1.0 in (25.4 mm)	4.5 ft (1.37 m)

SHAFT DIAMETER inches or mm	MAXIMUM BEARING SPACING feet or meters (cont.)
1.5 in (38 mm)	5.5 ft (1.70 m)
2.0 in (51 mm)	6.5 ft (2.0 m)
2.5 in (64 mm)	7.5 ft (2.3 m)

This list is intended only as a guide and the shaft manufacturers should be consulted for each boat.

Careful attention must be given to installations where the engine is well forward in the hull or when the engine is at the transom and a V-drive is used. Bearings inside the hull are required on both types of installations.

SUMMARY

This chapter has shown the relationships of boat speed and a new method of estimating speeds of new boats. Calculations for propeller size and reduction gear ratio have shown the interaction of horsepower, boat speed and propeller size. All of this is extremely important in a successful boat.

BOAT SPEED			
LB/HP	KG/HP	SPEED-LENGTH RATIO	
		English	Metric
960	436	0.9	3
667	303	1	3.35
500	227	1.17	3.9
350	159	1.5	5
200	91	2	6.7
150	68	2.25	7.5
100	45	2.6	8.7
LB/HP	KG/HP	Knots	Km/hr
75	34	19.6	36
50	23	24	44
40	18	26.8	50
30	14	30	55.5
20	9	38	70
15	7	43.8	81
10	4.5	53.6	99
8	3.6	60	111
6	2.7	69.2	128
5	2.3	76	140
4	1.8	84.8	157

Figure 8-1

The table is entered with the desired speed and boat weight to obtain the required horsepower. The manufacturer's advertise HP rating is used. When LB/HP is between 75 and 100, use an average of speeds from $V/L^{.5} = 2.6$ and from $V^2 (LB/HP) = 28750$.

MINIMUM PROPELLER DIAMETER			
AREA OF LARGEST HULL SECTION		MINIMUM DIAMETER	
Sq feet	Sq meters	Inches	Centimeters
5	0.47	12	31
10	0.93	17	43
20	1.86	24	61
30	2.79	29	75
40	3.72	34	86
50	4.65	38	96
60	5.58	42	106
70	6.51	45	114
80	7.44	48	122
90	8.37	51	129
100	9.3	54	136

Figure 8-2

Then minimum propeller diameter is only a guide for determination of the required reduction gear. Enter the table of propeller diameters with the minimum diameter and the horsepower of one engine. The required propeller RPM can then be observed from the table. The reduction gear ratio is the maximum engine RPM divided by the required propeller RPM.

PROPELLER PITCH IN INCHES/CENTIMETERS								
RPM	Hull Type	Boat Speed In Knots/Km Per Hour						
		5/9.3	10/18.5	15/21.8	20/37.1	25/46.4	30/55.6	40/74.2
900 RPM	Disp	12/30	25/64	36/91	48/122			
	Avg	10/25	20/51	30/76	40/102			
	Plan	9/23	16/41	24/61	32/81			
1200 RPM	Disp	10/25	18/46	27/69	36/91	45/114		
	Avg	8/20	15/38	23/58	30/76	38/97		
	Plan	6/15	12/30	19/48	24/61	30/76		
1500 RPM	Disp	7/18	15/38	21/53	29/74	36/91	43/109	
	Avg	6/15	12/30	18/46	24/61	30/76	36/91	
	Plan	5/13	10/25	15/38	20/51	24/61	29/74	
1800 RPM	Disp		12/30	18/46	24/61	30/76	36/91	48/122
	Avg		10/25	15/38	20/51	25/64	30/76	40/102
	Plan		8/20	12/30	16/41	20/51	24/61	32/81
2100 RPM	Disp		11/28	15/38	20/51	25/64	31/79	41/104
	Avg		9/23	13/33	17/43	21/53	26/65	34/87
	Plan		7/18	11/28	14/36	17/43	21/53	27/69
2400 RPM	Disp		9.5/24	13/33	18/46	22/56	27/69	36/91
	Avg		8/20	11/28	15/38	19/48	22/56	30/76
	Plan		6.5/16	9/23	12/30	16/41	18/46	24/61
3000 RPM	Disp		7.5/19	11/28	14/36	18/46	22/56	29/74
	Avg		6/15	9/23	12/30	15/38	18/46	24/61
	Plan		5/13	7/18	10/25	12/30	14/36	19/40

Figure 8-3

Average Hull Pitch (in) = v kt x 1800 / rpm (semi-planning). Average Hull Pitch (in) = v km/hr x 2500 / rpm (semi-planning). Propeller pitch for a displacement hull is 20% greater and 20% less for a planing hull.

PROPELLER DIAMETER IN INCHES/CENTIMETERS									
HP	PROPELLER RPM								
	600	900	1,200	1,500	1,800	2,100	2,400	2,700	3,000
30	26/66	20/57	17/43	15/38	13/33	12/30	11.5/29	11/28	10/25
60	30/76	24/61	20/51	18/45	16/41	14/36	13/33	12.5/32	12/30
90	33/84	26/66	22/56	19/48	17/43	16/41	15/38	14/36	13/33
120	35/89	27/69	23/58	20/51	18/45	17/43	15.5/39	14.5/37	14/36
150	36/91	28.5/72	24/61	21/53	19/48	17.5/44	16/41	15/38	15/38
200	38/97	30/76	25/64	22/56	20/51	18/45	17/43	16/41	15.5/39
300	42/107	33/84	27.5/70	24/61	21.5/54	20/51	18.5/47	17.5/44	16.5/42
400	44/112	35/89	29/74	25.5/65	23/58	21/53	20/51	18.5/47	17.5/44
500	46/117	36/91	31/79	27/69	24/61	22/56	20.5/52	19/48	18.5/47
600	48/122	37/94	32/81	28/71	25/64	23/58	21/53	20/51	19/48
700	49/125	39/99	33/84	28.5/72	25.5/65	23.5/60	22/56	20.5/52	19.5/50
800	50/127	39.5/100	33.5/85	29/74	26/66	24/61	22.5/57	21/53	20/51
900	51/130	40/102	34/86	30/76	27/69	24.5/62	23/58	21.5/55	20.5/52
1,000	53/135	41/104	35/89	30.5	27.5/70	25/64	23.5/60	22/56	21/53

Figure 8-4

This chart shows the propeller diameter for various advertised engine HP and propeller RPM. Use only for inboard engines. Consult propeller manufacturer for each installation.

SHAFT DIAMETER IN INCHES/MILLIMETERS							
HP	Yield in Torsion	PROPELLER RPM					
		600	900	1,200	1,500	1,800	2,100
30	20/138	1.45/37	1.25/32	1.15/29	1.1/28	1/25	.95/24
	70/482	1/25	.83/21	.8/20	.7/18	.7/18	.63/16
60	20/138	1.8/46	1.6/41	1.45/37	1.34/34	1.3/33	1.2/31
	70/482	1.2/31	1.1/28	1/25	.9/23	.84/21	.8/20
90	20/138	2.1/53	1.8/46	1.65/42	1.54/39	1.45/37	1.37/35
	70/482	1.3/33	1.2/31	1.14/29	1.05/27	1/25	.9/23
120	20/138	2.3/59	2.0/51	1.8/46	1.7/43	1.6/41	1.5/38
	70/482	1.5/38	1.3/33	1.2/31	1.12/29	1.1/28	1.0/25
150	20/138	2.5/64	2.16/55	1.96/50	1.8/46	1.7/43	1.6/41
	70/482	1.6/41	1.4/36	1.3/33	1.2/31	1.1/28	1.1/28
200	20/138	2.7/69	2.4/61	2.15/55	2/51	1.9/48	1.8/46
	70/482	1.8/46	1.6/41	1.4/36	1.3/33	1.25/32	1.2/31
300	20/138	3.1/79	2.7/69	2.5/64	2.3/58	2.16/55	2.04/52
	70/482	2.1/53	1.8/46	1.6/41	1.5/38	1.4/36	1.35/34
400	20/138	3.4/81	3.0/76	2.7/69	2.5/64	2.36/60	2.25/57
	70/482	2.27/58	2/51	1.8/46	1.7/43	1.6/40	1.5/38
500	20/138	3.7/94	3.2/81	2.9/74	2.7/69	2.56/65	2.43/62
	70/482	2.44/62	2.1/53	1.9/48	1.8/46	1.7/43	1.6/41
600	20/138	3.9/99	3.4/81	3.1/79	2.9/74	2.7/69	2.6/66
	70/482	2.6/66	2.3/58	2.1/53	1.9/48	1.8/46	1.7/43
700	20/138	4.1/104	3.6/92	3.3/84	3/76	2.85/72	2.7/69
	70/482	2.73/70	2.4/61	2.2/58	2/51	1.9/48	1.8/46

Figure 8-5

Select material yield strength in torsion.
20 ksi = 138 MPa. 70 ksi = 482 MPa.
D^3 in = 321 (HP) FS = 3.8 / stress (ksi) rpm
D^3 mm = 3.6 x 10^7 (HP) FS = 3.8 / stress (MPa) rpm.

CHAPTER NINE

HULL LINES

All the material in the previous chapters is brought together to influence the shape of the hull. You will see how the hull shape varies with the speed of the boat, how the hull lines are drawn and how to change the hull lines to meet design requirements. Example hull lines are shown for both powerboats and sailboats.

The designer has wide latitude in the shape of the hull above the water but much less freedom with the underwater shapes. The constraints on the hull bottom shape are listed and then explained:

Hull length, beam and speed.
Hull displacement and longitudinal center of gravity (LCG).
The shape of the sheer line and chine line or designed waterline.
Round bilge or V-bottom.
Deadrise angle
Prismatic Coefficient

Hull <u>length and beam</u> are determined by the practical necessities of having sufficient room for the people, accommodations and other gear. Boat speed is selected to meet the owner's requirements.

The <u>weight of the boat</u>, as it will be operated and its LCG must be exactly matched by the underwater volume of the hull lines and the location of the center of this volume (<u>Longitudinal Center of Buoyancy</u> - LCB).

. The selection of a <u>round bilge</u> boat or a <u>V-bottom</u> hull can be made on the basis of minimum resistance or the ease of construction. Flat bottomed skiffs used in protected waters are certainly easier to build. Most will agree the canoe hull with its narrow beam and sharply pointed bow and stern is surely the most efficient for calm water and slow speeds but construction complexity is increased.

Photo 14   John P. Kaufman

Round bilge of a wooden powerboat.

Testing has shown a displacement speed hull has lower resistance with a round bottom and higher speed hulls should use a V-bottom (chine). Some builders may insist on V-bottom (chine) construction to reduce costs even on slow, displacement speed boats. In this case, the chine line (intersection of hull bottom and hull side) should slope up in profile as it runs from amidships to the stern (Figure 9-5). In a moderate speed boat, the chine should be parallel to the waterline (Figure 9-4) as it runs aft from amidships, in profile. In a planing hull (Figure 9-3), the chine should slope down slightly from amidships to the stern, as seen in profile.

In plan view, the <u>chine line</u> (or designed waterline) is drawn with almost a straight line in the forward ten percent of length but never with a hollow, concave shape. The maximum width is about amidships and it tapers inboard toward the stern. The <u>sheer line</u> is much fuller than the chine forward, in plan view but is generally parallel to the chine aft of amidships. In profile, the sheer line is taken from the styling drawing.

<u>Deadrise</u> is an odd word of undetermined origin but in boat design it means

the angle between the hull bottom at the stern and the horizontal. If the bottom sections are parallel throughout the aft forty percent of waterline length, the hull is said to have "constant deadrise" .Referring to Figures 9-3, 9-4 and 9-5, this principle of parallel bottom sections and 'constant deadrise" is designed into the hull lines of slow speed, medium speed and fast boats. In other words, the angle between the bottom sections and the horizontal is the same in the aft portions of the hull. This is good design practice, as it results in smooth, continuous water flow over the hull bottom in all types of boats.

High deadrise angles of more than 14 degrees can be used with hulls intended for continuous use in rough waters but their resistance in calm water will be much higher than with less deadrise angle. All other hulls intended for average use should have deadrise angles between 8 and 14 degrees. The exact angle is a matter of preference, with lower angles of deadrise being used in hulls that will be in relatively calm water. Angles less than 8 degrees produce a relatively flat bottom that will pound into the water at anything but slow speeds.

One of the most important hull design parameters is the <u>Prismatic Coefficient</u> (Cp). It is a measurement of the distribution of volume along the waterline length. It is sometimes called the "fineness coefficient" as it measures whether the forward or aft portions of the underwater volume are very full or very fine in relation to the midships portion. In actual practice, the forward portion of the underwater volume is usually pointed and rather fine in shape, so fullness reflected by this coefficient is mainly due to the shape aft of amidships. The prismatic coefficient (Cp) is a ratio of the underwater hull volume in cubic feet (m³) divided by the product of the waterline length multiplied by the area of the largest submerged hull section.

As an example, we have a planing powerboat with a 30 foot (9.15 m) waterline length and weight of 16,128 lbs, (7331 kg). The displacement in cubic feet (m³) is the weight divided by the weight of sea water. Thus, 16128 / 64 is 252 cuft (7.1m³). The maximum underwater section area of this hull is 12 sqft. (1.11m²).

The prismatic coefficient is: Cp = Displacement divided by (LWL x Max. Area.)

In our example; Cp = 252 / 12 x 30 = 0.7 or in metric; Cp = 7.1 / 1.11 x 9.15 = 0.7

The prismatic coefficient (Cp) is a dimensionless ratio and 0.7 is correct for a planing powerboat.

The resulting ratio must be 0.51 to 0.54 for sailboats, .54 to .60 for displacement speed powerboats, .60 to .68 for moderate speed powerboats and .68 to .72 for planing vessels. These values have shown to produce minimum hull resistance within their speed range. This is why the Cp is extremely important in good hull design.

DRAWING OF THE PRELIMINARY HULL LINES

Figure 9-2 shows how the hull lines drawing is started, using as large a scale as will fit the drawing board. First, a very accurate grid of straight lines should be drawn. These are the base line and waterlines in profile, centerline and buttock (butt) lines in plan view. Vertical section lines (0 - 10) are drawn in both views. Buttock (butt) lines define the intersection of the hull surface with fore-and-aft planes that are parallel to the boat's centerline. These lines are curved in the profile but straight in the plan view. The sections are sometimes called the "body plan" and they can be drawn on top of the profile, above the plan view or on a separate sheet. The sections of the sailboat in Figure 9-7 are drawn on a separate sheet and to a larger scale only for purposes of clarity in this book.

In plan view (as seen from above), the sheer line and approximation of the chine line are drawn (or the designed waterline in a round bilge hull). In profile, the sheer, stem and stern are taken from the styling drawing and an approximate chine line and hull bottom profile at the centerline is drawn. Preliminary sections (stations) are drawn using the height of the sheer and chine from the profile and half - breadths from the plan view. These sections are important in establishing the interior floor height, ensuring the interior joinerwork will fit and more importantly, calculating the displacement, LCB and prismatic coefficient (Cp).

DISPLACEMENT CALCULATIONS - LCB AND Cp

The total volume of the hull (displacement) must equal the weight of the boat. The volume and weight relationship is determined by the density of salt water, 64 pounds per cubic foot (1025 kg/m³). If a boat will be used in fresh water, use 62.4 lbs/ft³ (1000 kg/m³) (One metric ton/m³). The center of this volume (Center Of buoyancy - CB) must be in the same longitudinal location as the total center of gravity if the boat is to float level. If these two centers are not in alignment, the hull lines are re-drawn to achieve agreement. Also, if the Cp is not correct, the lines are re-drawn.

When the computer is used for hull lines, the required data is entered into the program and the calculations are quickly completed. When changes are necessary, they can be made on the computer in a shorter time than can be done manually on paper. After the design is established, the final fairing of the lines can be accomplished on the computer and most programs will print out a completed table of offsets, which will be explained later. Whatever method is used for hull lines and calculations, the designer must know the background of manual drawing as this is the operating basis for any computer program.

The area of each hull section is found to start the displacement calculation process. This can be done with a planimeter, a computer or by the triangulation method shown in Figure 5-3. These areas are then used with Simpson's Rule to find the displacement, CB and Cp, as shown in Figure 9-1. The half areas of each section are multiplied by Simpson's Numbers and then totaled. When this total is multiplied by one-third the station spacing and by two, the displacement is found in cubic feet (m³). When the previous numbers are multiplied by the station number (not the station spacing) and totaled, then divided by the total of the previous column, the center of buoyancy is found, in terms of the station numbers (0-10).

The displacement - length ratio is mentioned frequently in boating magazines but it is not a necessary part of hull design. It does provide a method of comparing one hull to another, if they are similar in length and use. This ratio is the displacement in long tons (2240 pounds) divided by the cube of the waterline length divided by 100. This ratio in metric terms is 28 kg / LWL (m³). A very light sailboat or racing powerboat may have a displacement - length ratio of 100 but a heavy motor sailor or a cruising powerboat may have this ratio equal to 350. A boat has to weigh what is necessary for its operation. The same length hull may be very heavy if it is a commercial fisherman but very light if it is a recreational sport fisherman.

This is the time to evaluate the entire design. Any changes are normally made by varying the width of the chine line, the height of the chine line and the draft. Figure 9-10 shows those changes that result in a selective change in hull volume.

When the displacement, CB and Cp are correct, the preliminary lines are ready for fairing. This will be explained for each of the drawings in Figures 9-3 through Figures 9-9.

CALCULATION OF DISPLACEMENT & CENTER OF BUOYANCY					
Station	Half Area of Section Sq Ft	Simpson's Numbers	Multiply to Get	Center of Bouyancy	
				Station	Multply
0	0	1	-----	0	-----
1	0.87	4	3.48	1	3.48
2	2	2	4	2	8
3	3.08	4	12.32	3	36.96
4	4.24	2	8.48	4	33.92
5	5.63	4	22.52	5	112.6
6	5.95	2	11.9	6	71.4
7	5.88	4	23.52	7	164.64
8	5.69	2	11.38	8	91.04
9	5.43	4	21.72	9	195.48
10	5.16	1	5.16	10	51.6
		Totals	124.48		769.12

Figure 9-1

36 Foot Planing powerboat. LWL = 32.5ft Station spacing is 3.25ft
Half Displacement = 124.48 x 3.25 / 3 = 134.85 cuft
Full Displacement = 269.7cuft = 17,261 lb = 7.7 long tons.
CB = 769.12 / 124.48 = station 6.179.
Prismatic Coefficient = Displacement / Largest area x LWL = 269.7 / 11.9 x
32.5 = 0.697.
Displacement - Length Ratio = 7.7 / .0343 = 224.48.

PLANING POWERBOAT HULL LINES

Figure 9-3 shows a 32.5 foot (l0 m) waterline length fast powerboat where the chine line slopes down in profile as it runs aft from station 6 to station 10. The aft portion of the hull bottom almost shows as one line in the sections. This is very desirable in a fast hull. The shape of the sheer line is only one example of many choices.

The designed waterline is 24 inches (.6 m) above the base line (keel) and other waterlines are shown at 36 in (.9 m) and 60 in (1.5 m) above the base line. Additional fairing of the hull lines is accomplished with butt lines at 24 in (.6 m) and 48 in (1.2 m) out from the centerline. The height of the intersection of the butt with the stations is taken from the sections (body plan) and plotted on the profile drawing. The intersection of the butt with the waterlines in plan view must be at the same longitudinal position as in the profile view. Note the 48 in (1.2 m) butt line intersects the chine line slightly aft of station 9. This point must agree in all three views.

One diagonal fairing line is shown extending down from the 36 in (.9 m) waterline on the sections in Figure 9-3. It is located by choice to intersect the hull bottom at close to a right angle. For convenience, the diagonal is drawn from the boat centerline at an existing waterline. It usually intersects the base line at a butt line. The intersection of this diagonal with each section is measured from the centerline along the diagonal. It is then plotted at each section, above the plan view, taking care it meets the centerline at the waterline from which it was drawn. The diagonal must be perfectly fair without any humps or hollows.

This fairing process is the same for all hulls, whether V-bottom (chine) or round bottom as all the hull lines use the same grid of sections, waterlines, butt lines and diagonals. Usually, two or three diagonals are drawn and the spacing of waterlines and butt lines is not more than 12 inches (.3 m). For clarity, only two waterlines are shown in Figure 9-3. The waterline width at each station (section) is plotted on the plan view to produce an absolutely fair line. The designed waterline on which the boat must float is shown as the 24 inch (.6 m) waterline. This designed waterline is seldom drawn in V-bottom hulls as it is concave forward of the intersection with the chine line. This may look odd but it is a normal shape.

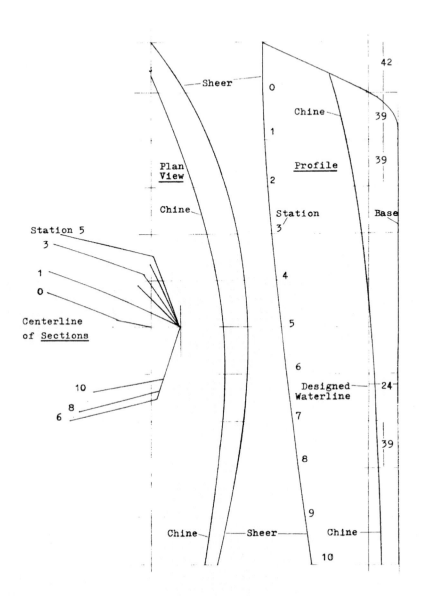

Figure 9-2

Preliminary hull lines. 36 ft planing powerboat. LWL 32.5, Beam 13 ft, Draft 2 ft, V / LWL$^{.5}$ = 5.0, Disp. = 17,261 lb.

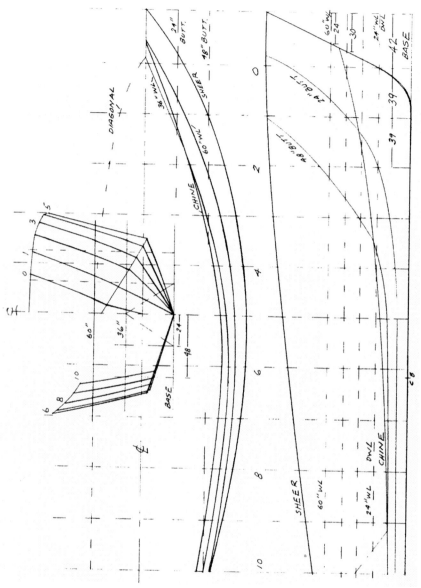

Figure 9-3

36 ft planing powerboat. LWL 32.5, Beam 13 ft, Draft 2 ft, $V / LWL^{.5} = 5.0$, Disp. = 17,261 lb, Cp = .697, CB = 6.18

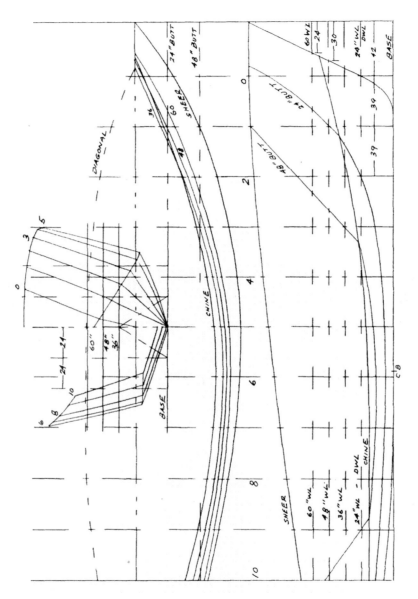

Figure 9-4

36 ft semi-planing powerboat. LWL 32.5, V / LWL$^{.5}$ = 2.5, Disp. = 17,130 lb Cp = .65, CB = .59.

MODERATE SPEED POWERBOAT HULL LINES

Figure 9-4, above, shows a 32.5 foot (10 m) waterline length powerboat designed for moderate speed. The chine line is approximately parallel to the designed waterline as it runs aft, in profile. In section, the hull bottom at the stern is parallel to and slightly above the hull bottom at station 6. This parallelism in the aft sections is desirable in all hull forms, at all speeds. It shows the water flow is uniformly distributed over the hull bottom as the water is moving aft. If the aft sections of the hull bottom are not parallel, the hull is said to have a "warped bottom" .This results in the water flow being directed up near the centerline and down near the chine line. This causes a variation in pressure over the hull bottom and increased resistance will result. This point shows another reason why boats with the same weight and horsepower will have varying speeds.

By coincidence in Figure 9-4, note the 48 inch (1.2m) waterline, the 24 inch (.6 m) butt and station 1 all intersect at the same point in all three views. This is also true with the 36 inch (.9 m) waterline, station 3 and the 48 inch (1.2 m) butt. These are obvious fairing points that make the fairing process somewhat easier to define. The widths of the chine and waterlines in the plan view and the height of the chine in profile are all transferred to the sections. The width and height of the sheer line are similarly put on the sections drawing. The intersections of the butt lines in section and plan are transferred to the profile drawing. All must be fair, smooth lines.

DISPLACEMENT SPEED POWERBOAT HULL LINES

Figure 9-5 shows the hull lines of a 32.5 foot (10 m) waterline powerboat with a speed - length ratio of 1.2. In profile, the chine line slopes up, above the designed waterline, as it runs aft from amidships. The aft portion of the hull bottom lines are parallel in section, giving clean water flow.

Note the aft portion of the hull volume becomes less as we make the transition from planing hull to displacement hull (Figures 9-3, 9-4, 9-5). This change in volume aft, results in the correct Cp for minimum resistance. Also note the aft portion of the hull lines retain the parallelism in all three views. It is a mistake to think that the bottom at the stern has to be horizontal.

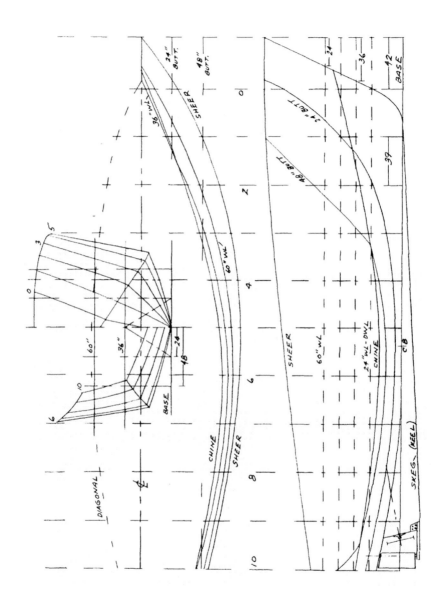

Figure 9-5

36 ft Displacement powerboat, LWL 32.5 ft, Disp. 16,300, V / LWL·⁵ = 1.2, Cp = .537, CB = 5.4

A keel is shown in Figure 9-5 to protect the propeller. This is normal in displacement powerboats and the total draft must be measured to the lowest point of the keel. The surface area of the hull in the water (wetted surface) is increased by installing a keel but the protection for the propeller is an absolute necessity and far outweighs the small increase in frictional resistance. In addition, it has been found a displacement or moderate speed hull will steer much easier under autopilot if there is a keel. The increased cost of new construction will be much less than subsequent repair bills.

SAILBOAT HULL LINES

Figures 9-6 and 9-7 show the hull lines for a 28.33 foot (8.9 m) waterline cruising sailboat. The lines are arranged on the drawing in a manner which is convenient. The placing of the diagonals above the plan view and the sections on a separate sheet is just a matter of preference. The sections are shown in a larger scale only for purposes of clarity in this book. Note the hull portion forward and aft of the waterline endings (overhangs) can be any length which looks good in the styling drawing. The station spacing for ten stations is a constant 34 inches (.89 m). (28.33 ft LWL (8.9 mm) = 340 inches (8.9 m). The forward ends of the waterline on centerline should be as sharp as possible for minimum resistance (one half inch (1.27 cm) radius for glass fiber hull). Above the waterline, these waterline endings can be rounded with a progressively larger radius if a large radius at the deck is desired. The waterlines are convex, never concave.

The designed waterline and sheer are drawn in plan view and the sheer and the hull bottom at centerline are drawn in profile. Using these points at each station, the heights and widths are transferred to the sections. The sectional shape of the hull is approximated between these three points and preliminary calculations are made for displacement, CB and Cp. If all three are correct, the hull fairing process begins with the waterlines, butt lines and diagonals.

The profile area of one side of the keel below the hull proper is usually 25 to 80 percent of the underwater profile area of the hull alone, not including the rudder. Centerboards, outside any keel area, are usually at the low end of this area approximation. Deep, narrow keels on racing sailboats are sometimes half the area of a long keel on a cruising sailboat. Keels that run the full waterline length are unusual today but their area may be more than that of the underwater profile of the hull alone.

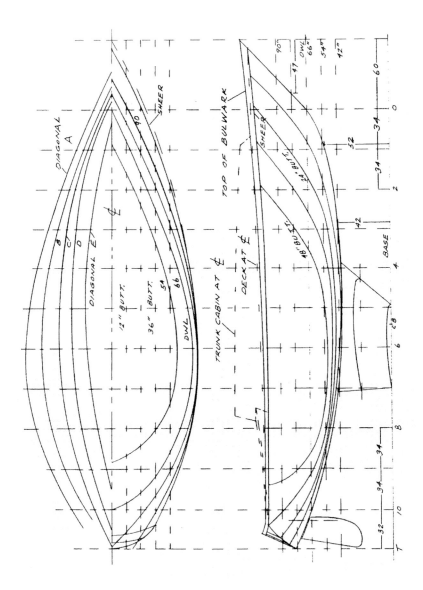

Figure 9-6

36 ft Cruising sailboat.

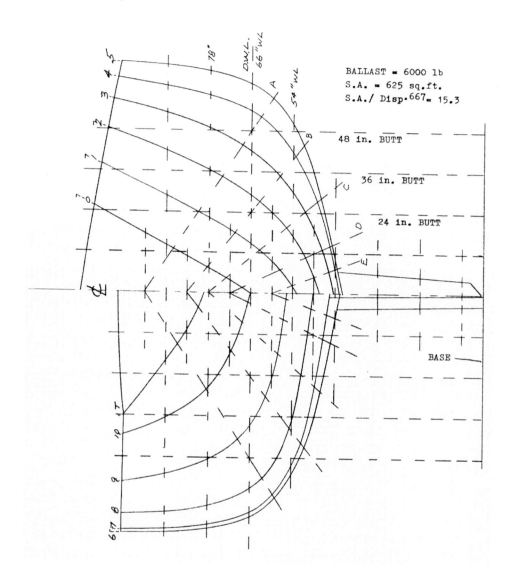

BALLAST = 6000 lb
S.A. = 625 sq.ft.
S.A./ Disp.^{667} = 15.3

Figure 9-7

36 ft Cruising sailboat sections, ballast 6000lb, SA 625 sqft, SA / Disp.^{667} = 15.3 LOA 36 ft, Beam 11.8 ft, LWL 28.33 ft, Draft 5.5 ft, Disp 16,750 lb, Cp = .513, CB = 5.43.

The purpose of keels and centerboards is to reduce leeway induced by the athwartships component of sail forces, in addition to the keel containing the ballast at the lowest possible location. Both should be thin, hydrodynamic shapes with parabolic leading edges and sharp trailing edges. Centerboards should not float but they should not be of heavy construction material as there would be excessive loads on the pivot pin and the hull structure. Solid glass fiber with a density of 96 pounds per cubic foot (1535 kg/m³) (average laminate) is an ideal material for centerboards.

The profile of the hull lines in Figure 9-6 shows the top of the toe rail or bulwark, as this tells the builder there is a toe rail above the deck at the side (sheer) and it shows the shape of this line. The top of the bulwark is not usually parallel to the sheer and it is normally twice the height at the bow as at the stern. The forward end of the lines drawing may be at the intersection of the stem and sheer or at the intersection of the bulwark and stem. (Figure 9-6) These comments on bulwarks apply to powerboats as well as sailboats, although the bulwark on a powerboat is usually just in the forward half of the length.

The height of the trunk cabin and the cockpit coaming are also shown on the hull lines drawing so the builder can establish the relationship of deck and hull. This also provides the information needed to plan the required height for his building shop. The height of the deck at centerline is shown in profile to fix the deck camber the designer considers appropriate. This line may be straight or curved longitudinally, as a matter of preference. The lines of the deck are drawn by placing the deck at centerline height on four or five sections and drawing a radius to the sheer. Preliminary butt lines are then transferred to the profile and faired continuously from stem to stern as if there were no interruptions for a cockpit or deck house. These deck structures are then located after deck fairing.

The transom at centerline may be raked aft or forward or it may be vertical, as shown on the styling drawing. The athwartships curvature of the transom is drawn as a radius on the plan view from the points of intersection of the centerline with the sheer and waterlines on the profile drawing. A constant radius of any desired dimension is used and the resulting shape is the surface of a cylinder, tilted forward or aft. These arcs of a circle are drawn to intersect the waterlines in plan view, thus fixing the outboard edges of the transom. (Figure 9-6) These points are then transferred back to the profile at the waterlines.

CATAMARANS AND TRIMARANS

The main hull of a trimaran, on the boat centerline, is similar to that of a monohull and can be either round or "V" bottom, as the designer prefers. The outboard hulls (floats) are normally narrow in beam and can be shaped like catamaran hulls, not necessarily symmetrical about each hull centerline. Multihulls can be powerboats or sailboats designed for any speed.

Each designer has a wide selection for the shape of a catamaran hull, as illustrated in Figure 9-11. Some alternatives are shown and each has the same sectional area. They are drawn on the same centerline so comparisons may be more obvious. A conventional "V" bottom is shown in (1) and the almost rectangular section results in minimum draft. The rounded, "V" hull of (2) has been used by many designers for sailing catamarans.

The asymmetric catamaran hull shapes in (4) and (5) show much less volume on the inboard side which makes a larger opening between hulls. This wider space allows any bow wave to flow more freely to the stern without slamming against the hulls or the connecting structure (wing) between the two hulls. In addition, the curvature on the inboard side provides some lift to windward on sailing catamarans. This lift is on the windward side of the leeward hull and helps to reduce leeway. Hull forms (4) or (5) can be with chines or round. The deeper draft of (5) is normally not a problem as the propeller will extend to a depth at or below the hull.

Any catamaran hull will be slowed considerably if waves between the hulls impact the hulls or connecting structure. To keep a wide space between hulls, it is recommended the minimum horizontal distance between the inboard sides of the catamaran hulls is 0.2 multiplied by the overall length of the boat. (LOA), measured at the waterline. The minimum height of the bottom of the connecting structure (wing) above the designed waterline should be 0.1 LOA.

The advantages of a multihull are a wide deck space and less tendency to roll. This is accomplished by two or more hulls, widely spaced, with a strong connecting structure. Usually this means greater construction costs than a monohull but the advantages are often more important for many applications. To appreciate these benefits, the overall beam of the boat should be at least 40 to 50 percent of the overall length. Designing a narrow beam for a multihull is a waste of effort as all the benefits of a multihull will be lost.

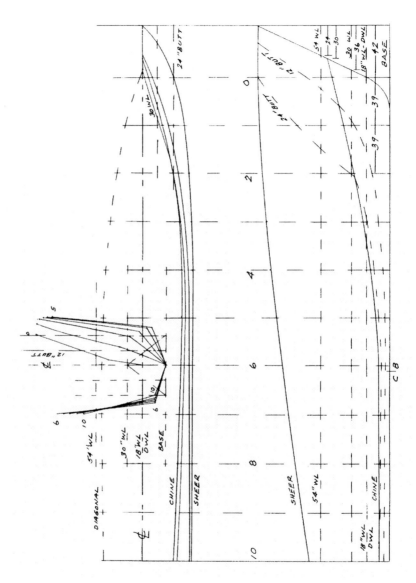

Figure 9-8

36 ft Catamaran, LWL 32.5, V / LWL.⁵ = 2.3, Disp 17,160 (two hulls), Cp = .688 (one hull), CB = 6.1.

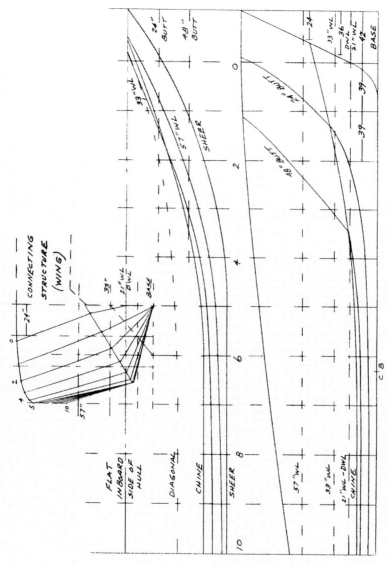

Figure 9-9

36 ft Catamaran, LWL 32.5, V / LWL.⁵ = 2.8, Disp 17,400 (two hulls), Cp = .70, CB = .63.

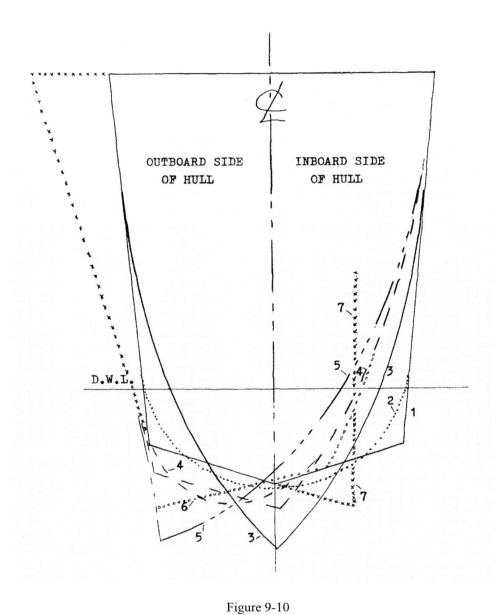

OUTBOARD SIDE
OF HULL

INBOARD SIDE
OF HULL

D.W.L.

Figure 9-10

Catamaran hull shapes with the same sectional area.

Figure 9-8 shows a conventional hull form for a fast catamaran. All the rules of displacement, CB and Cp hold true for multihulls just as with monohulls. The chine is shown parallel to the waterline for use with a moderate speed, semi-planing, hull. If the chine were to slope down slightly in the aft sections, the hull bottom would show as one line in the sections. This is the correct procedure for a planing hull.

Photo 15   John P. Kaufman

Powerboat catamaran hull.

Figure 9-8 is a similar hull form to (1) in Figure 9-11 and (7) is similar to Figure 9-9. This latter asymmetric hull, as well as (4) and (5), show much less volume inside the hull, above the waterline, on the inboard side. They show equal volume if the beam is increased on the outboard side of each hull. Beam at the deck level is a matter of choice in a catamaran. The minimum spacing between hulls, measured at the waterline, is the critical dimension in catamarans.

With a speed - length ratio of 2.8, the hull lines in Figure 9-9 represent a boat that is almost planing. It is judgmental whether the aft portion of the chine should be level or sloped down. This is a case where either shape would be acceptable. Most of the time the hull would travel at less than top speed and a level chine aft is probably justified. The asymmetric hull has been used with considerable success in both power and sailing catamarans. The beam of each hull is a matter of providing adequate space inside each hull, depending on the requirements of loading. If a narrower hull can be tolerated, a wider spacing between the inboard sides of the hulls and lower resistance for each hull will result.

TABLE OF OFFSETS

After the hull lines are complete, the heights of the sheer, chine and butt lines at each station are measured. The width of the sheer, chine and waterlines at each station are measured. All of these are entered into a table called the "Table of Offsets" which are shown in Figure 9-12. The builder uses these dimensions to draw the hull lines full size on a floor (lofting). The drawing of the hull lines are thus reproduced with great accuracy for the purpose of making frame patterns.

When the builder sets the bulkheads and frames vertically on a foundation prior to making the hull, the edges must be absolutely accurate. When a long batten is placed over these frame edges, any variation from fairness will be immediately apparent. Thus the hull lines must be carefully drawn to get good accuracy.

36 FT CRUISING SAILBOAT - ROUND BILGE											
OFFSETS IN FT-INCHES-EIGHTHS : + IS 1/16 INCH											
Half Breadths	0	1	2	3	4	5	6	7	8	9	10
54" WL	-----	0-1-7+	1-5-2	2-6-3	3-6-6	4-2-7	4-5-7	4-3-2+	3-2-1	-----	-----
66" WL (DWL)	-----	1-3-0	2-5-2	3-6-3	4-6-0	5-2-1	5-5-4	5-4-1+	4-9-3	3-3-2	-----
78" WL	0-7-2	1-10-6+	3-0-5	4-0-4	4-11-0	5-6-0	5-8-7	5-7-7+	5-2-2	4-0-4+	2-3-4
90" WL	1-2-2+	2-5-2	3-6-2	4-4-6	5-1-4	5-7-2	5-9-5+	5-8-7+	5-4-0	4-4-7+	3-0-4+
Sheer	2-1-4	3-2-2	4-0-5+	4-9-0+	5-3-4	5-8-0	5-10-1	5-9-2	5-4-5+	4-7-3	3-5-5
Heights											
12" Butts	7-2-0	5-2-3+	4-2-6	3-9-1	3-6-6	3-6-1	3-6-6	3-9-0+	4-1-4	4-8-7+	5-9-0
24" Butts	8-11-3+	6-8-1	4-11-7+	4-2-1	3-9-6	3-8-6	3-8-7+	3-11-0	4-3-1+	4-11-0+	6-3-1
36" Butts	-----	8-7-3	6-4-6	4-10-5	4-2-2	3-11-6	3-11-2	4-1-1	4-5-4	5-3-6	7-5-0
48" Butts	-----	-----	8-8-2	6-4-5+	4-10-1	4-4-2+	4-3-0	4-4-4	4-9-6+	6-4-7	-----
Sheer	9-2-2	9-0-0	8-10-0+	8-5-5	8-7-5	8-7-0	8-6-4+	8-6-2	8-5-7+	8-5-5	8-5-4
Diagonals											
A	1-3-3	2-4-6	3-4-7	4-3-7	5-1-6	5-8-1	5-10-5	5-9-4	5-3-6+	4-2-3	2-9-0
B	0-9-3	1-10-6	2-10-1	3-7-6	4-3-4+	4-7-4	4-8-6	4-6-7	4-1-2+	3-2-1	1-9-3
C	0-6-4+	1-7-4	2-5-5	3-0-7+	3-5-5+	3-7-1	3-7-1	3-4-7	3-0-0	2-3-0	1-1-3+
D	0-3-5	1-3-7	2-0-2+	2-5-4+	2-8-1	2-8-6	2-8-1+	2-5-7	2-1-2	1-5-3	0-6-1
E	-----	0-6-2	1-1-1+	1-5-5	1-7-5	1-8-2	1-7-3+	1-5-0	1-0-3	0-4-5	-----

Figure 9-12

CHANGES TO THE PRELIMINARY HULL LINES TO PRODUCE THE DESIRED CHARACTERISTICS

REQUIREMENTS & CHANGES TO BE MADE

More displacement
CB forward
Cp higher
Wider chine line in the forward sections

More displacement
CB forward
Cp same
Wider chine line in the forward sections and wider at mid-ship sections.

More displacement
CB forward
Cp lower
Wider chine line in the forward and middle sections, or narrow chine aft & more draft.

More displacement
CB must move aft
Cp higher
Wider chine line at aft sections.

More displacement
CB must move aft
Cp same
Wider chine line at aft and middle sections.

More displacement
CB must move aft
Cp lower
Wider chine in aft and middle sections, or less chine width forward and greater draft.

More displacement
CB same
Cp same
More Draft.

More displacement
CB same
Cp higher
Narrower chine line midships and more draft.

More displacement
CB same
Cp lower
Wider chine line (or DWL) amidships.

Same displacement
CB forward
Cp higher
Wider chine line at forward sections and less draft.

Same displacement
CB forward
Cp same
Narrower chine line at aft and slightly wider chine line at forward sections.

Same displacement
CB forward
Cp lower
Narrower chine line at aft sections and more draft.

Same displacement
CB must move aft
Cp higher
Wider chine line aft and less draft.

Same displacement
CB must move aft
Cp same
Wider chine line aft and narrower chine line at forward sections.

Same displacement
CB must move aft
Cp lower
Narrower chine line at forward sections and slightly more draft.

Same displacement
CB same
Cp higher
Narrower chine line amidships and slightly more draft.

Same displacement
CB same
Cp lower
Wider chine line amidships and slightly less draft.

Less displacement
CB must move forward
Cp higher
Wider chine line at forward sections and less draft.

Less displacement
CB must move forward
Cp same
Narrower chine line aft and amidships.

Less displacement
CB must move forward
Cp lower
Narrower chine line at aft sections.

Less displacement
CB must move aft
Cp higher
Wider chine at aft stations less draft.

Less displacement
CB must move aft
Cp same
Narrower chine line at forward and amidships sections.

Less displacement
CB must move aft
Cp lower
Narrower chine line forward.

Less displacement
CB same
Cp same
Less Draft.

Less displacement
CB same
Cp higher
Narrower chine line amidships.

Less displacement
CB same
Cp lower
Wider chine line at amidships sections and less draft.

Figure 9-10

SUMMARY

This chapter has shown examples of hull lines for sailboats and powerboats. Efficient hulls are produced when the hull shape is changed to match the range of operating speed. The fundamental factors of weight, LCG and LCB, deadrise angle and prismatic coefficient have been explained and illustrated.

Preliminary hull lines are drawn and corrected, until these fundamental factors are satisfactory. Final lines are then drawn with additional waterlines, butt lines and diagonals so each line is a fair, smooth curve and to be certain all three views of the hull lines are in agreement. The principles of hull shape explained in this chapter can be used with any type of hull in any range of speed.

CHAPTER TEN

STABILITY

The stability of a boat is defined as the ability to return to level flotation after being heeled over by the forces of wind and waves. This chapter will show the interaction of forces on the boat that produce this stability and how to find them. When the stability calculations have been made it is necessary to evaluate the results for different hull types and these criteria will be discussed. It is important to know what degree of stability is adequate and how it may be improved.

THE FORCES OF STABILITY

The position of the vertical center of gravity (VCG) was found in *Chapter Five*. It is assumed to be on the boat's centerline if weights on the boat are secured and not allowed to move to one side when the boat is heeled. The total weight of the boat is concentrated at the VCG and it acts vertically downward, perpendicular to any heeled waterline.

At the same time, the buoyant force of the water acts in a vertical line upward through the heeled center of buoyancy (CB) as shown on Figure 10-2. These two forces form a moment of forces which returns the boat to a level condition. The horizontal distance between these two forces is called the Righting Arm, which is abbreviated GZ and is the key to the measurement of stability. Figures 10-1 and 10-2 show the lines of a sailboat but the stability calculations are the same for any type of hull.

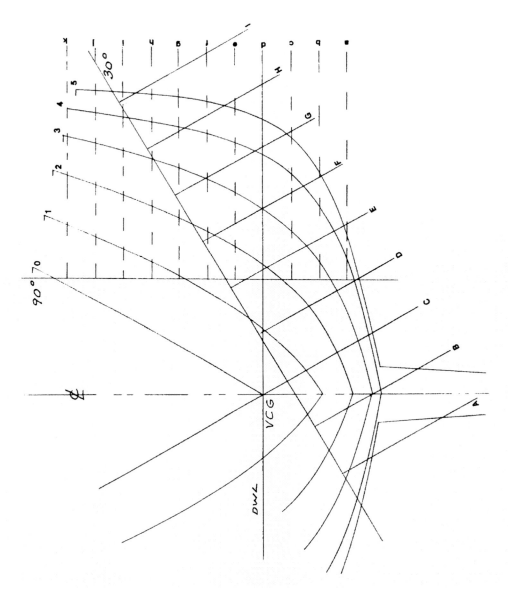

Figure 10-1

Stability sections for the forward half of the boat. This is the same hull as in Figures 9-6 & 9-7. Heeled waterlines at 30 degrees and 90 degrees are shown.

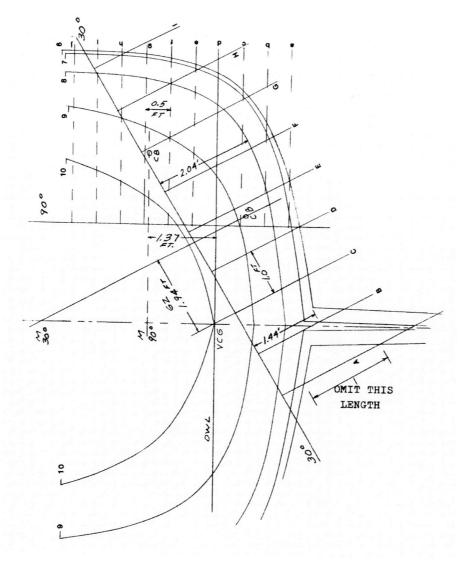

Figure 10-2

Aft stability sections for the same boat as Figures 10-1, 9-6 & 9-7.

CALCULATING THE RIGHTING ARM (GZ)

The height of the VCG is fixed on most hulls and the stability calculations involve finding the transverse position of the CB, to determine GZ. The calculations for hull displacement and LCB in *Chapter Nine* used transverse stations to find the longitudinal position of the center of buoyancy (LCB). In stability calculations, the same procedure is followed but using longitudinal stations to find the transverse position of the CB. The calculations proceed in the following steps:

Draw the forward sections of the hull on one sheet and the aft sections on another. Figures 10-1 and 10-2. This avoids the confusion of lines.

Find the location of the heeled waterlines to the correct displacement. At least three waterlines are used, normally 30, 60 and 90 degrees heel, from the horizontal.

At each waterline, draw any number of equally spaced longitudinal stations, with one station passing through the VCG, perpendicular to waterline.

Measure and record the depth of each transverse section at each longitudinal station, (Figure 10-3) below the heeled waterline.

Calculate the area of each longitudinal station.

Multiply the station area by its distance from the VCG. Total the results on each side of the VCG and subtract the smaller from the larger. The righting arm (GZ) equals this value divided by the total of the areas of the longitudinal stations. Figure 10-3. A discussion of these steps may be helpful.

For clarity, the forward and aft sections of the boat are drawn on separate sheets of paper. Also for clarity, only two heeled waterlines are shown on Figures 10-1 and 10-2. These heeled waterlines must be at the boat's displacement and they do not cross the upright waterline at the centerline. Two or three attempts with the planimeter may be necessary to find the correct location for these heeled waterlines. Computer programs are available for the calculation of stability, which do save time when the hull lines are in a computer data file.

In Figures 10-1 and 10-2, the longitudinal stations are spaced 1.0 feet (.3 m) apart on the 30 degree heeled waterline and 0.5 feet (.15 m) on the 90 degree heeled waterline, only by choice. The depth of each section at each longitudinal station multiplied by the transverse section spacing gives the area of each longitudinal station. The transverse center of displacement (CB) (Center Of Buoyancy) is found by multiplying each station area by its individual distance to the VCG. The total of these moments is then divided by the total station area. The table of Figure 10-3 is repeated for each angle of heel investigated. Some designers may calculate at every ten degrees of heel but at least three heeled waterlines are required.

STA	A	B	C	D	E	F	G	H	I	J	K
			TABLE FOR DETERMINING RIGHTING ARM AT ONE ANGLE OF HEEL								
0											
1			0.38	0.12							
2		0.7	1.04	1.04	0.74	0.24					
3	0.15	1.2	1.47	1.62	1.56	1.24	0.64				
4	0.52	1.36	1.68	1.98	1.12	2.08	1.66	0.78			
5	2.2	2.12	1.76	2.08	2.32	2.45	2.3	1.6	0.34		
6	1.92	2	1.73	2.08	2.4	2.56	2.52	2	0.74		
7	0.48	1.44	1.52	1.9	2.25	2.46	2.44	1.88	0.6		
8		0.6	1.1	1.5	1.76	2.04	1.94	1.22			
9			0.4	0.8	1.06	1.06	0.66				
10	SUMS OF AREAS (below) = 250.87 x 64 = 16,056 pounds										
Sum	5.27	9.42	11.08	13.12	14.21	14.13	12.16	7.48	1.68	2.83 ft = Area	
Area	14.93	26.69	31.39	37.17	40.26	40.03	34.45	21.19	4.76	Sum = 250.87	
Long Sta/ft	2	1	0	1	2	3	4	5	6	Moment Sum = 510.09 - 56.55 =	
Mom	29.86	26.69	0	37.17	80.52	120.09	137.8	105.95	28.56	453	

Figure 10-3

36 ft LOA Cruising sailboat, ballast 6000 lb, Beam 11.8 ft, LWL 28.33 ft, Disp 16,750 lb, angle of heel = 30 degrees, Longitudinal stations = 1.0 ft, GZ = 453 / 250.87 = 1.81. Transverse stations = 2.83 ft.

EVALUATING STABILITY

Each righting arm (GZ) is plotted on a graph at its angle of heel. Figure 10-4. The area under the resulting curve is calculated (shaded area) to the smaller of: Forty degrees; the angle where GZ is maximum; or the heel angle where water starts to flow into the hull (downflooding).

This area under the righting arm (GZ) curve is called the Rahola Criterion, after the man which first proposed this evaluation. It is now accepted world-wide. This area represents the righting energy after the boat is heeled by the wind or waves and must be greater than 15 foot - degrees (4.6 m-degrees). This evaluation applies to all types of boats, power and sail.

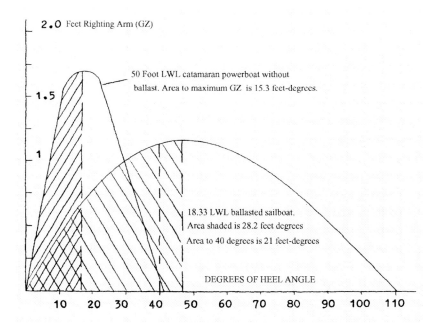

Figure 10-4

Curve of Righting Arms (GZ) at various angles of heel. The Rahola Criterion is illustrated to the maximum GZ and to 40 degrees. The length of Righting Arm and the heel angle of zero Righting Arm are as varied as there are types of boats.

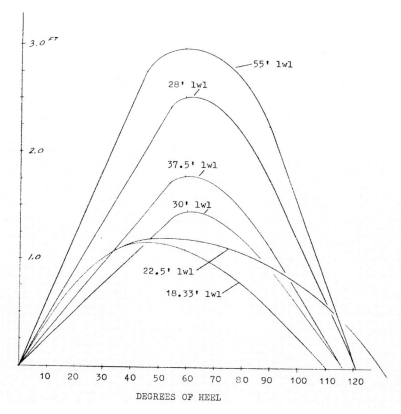

Figure 10-5

Curves of Righting Arms (feet) for a few powerboats (not ballasted). Note there is little similarity between types of hulls or waterline length. All but the lower two would satisfy the Rahola Criterion.

In addition to the above, a different type of stability evaluation must be considered for all types of hulls. This is the range of stability where the righting arm (GZ) becomes zero at some angle of heel. Figures 10-5 and 10-6, show this range of stability is not consistent for unballasted powerboats but ballasted sailboats must have a range greater than 100 degrees. The latter is necessary as sailboats will be hit by a gust of wind which will put the top of the mast in the water.

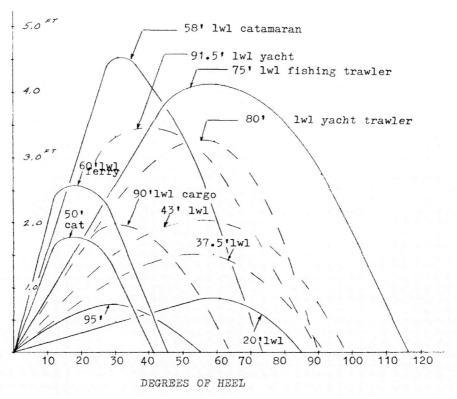

Figure 10-6

Curves of Righting Arms (feet) for a few sailboats with ballast.

When a powerboat will be used on the open ocean, the range of stability must be greater than seventy degrees. If it is not, the boat should be confined to protected waters. An alternative, with any type of hull, is to add ballast to lower the VCG. This increases the righting arm (GZ) as the VCG is farther away from the CB and the range of stability is also increased.

Some sailboats use port and starboard water tanks to keep a lower angle of heel when sailing to windward. You cannot be sure these tanks will be full or if the water weight will be shifted as the boat tacks. VCG and stability calculations should be done with all tanks empty.

MULTIHULL STABILITY IN SAILBOATS

Multihulls are normally without ballast and they <u>will capsize</u> if heeled by a strong wind or a large, cresting ocean wave. Multihulls tend to float parallel to the surface of the water and if that surface is a large, steep, ocean wave, the boat may capsize. This should be clearly explained to all multihull owners. A ballasted hull will heel in a cresting wave but the ballast will keep the hull at a lower angle of heel. Multihulls should conform to the Rahola Criterion (Figure 10-4) and ballast can be added to increase the range of stability, in both powerboats and sailboats.

Good seamanship and the ability of the crew are an important part of sailing multihull success. The windward hull should be in the water at all times and if lifted clear, the mainsheet is slacked and the sails reefed.

In a sailing multihull, the righting moment (energy) must be more than the heeling moment. The righting moment may be approximated by taking moments around the inboard side of the leeward hull (Figure 10-7). If we consider a 20 foot (6.1 m) beam sailing catamaran with 6 foot (1.83 m) beam hulls and 14,000 pound (6350 kg) displacement, the weight of the wing structure of 4000 pounds (1816 kg) produces a moment of 16,000 foot-pounds (2208 kg-m). If one hull weighs 5000 pounds (2270 kg) and has a moment arm of 11 feet (3.36 m), it contributes 55,000 foot-pounds (7590 kg-m) of righting moment, bringing the total to 71,000 foot-pounds (9823 kg-m).

This total must be more than the heeling moment of total sail area multiplied by a wind pressure of 1.6 pounds per square foot (.1 kPa) at 20 knots, multiplied by a heeling arm of 30 feet (9.15 m), multiplied by a factor of safety of 2.0. Heeling Moment = Righting Moment and Heeling Moment = SA x 2.0 x 1.6 x Heeling Arm. The Heeling Arm is measured from the center of effort of the sail area (*Chapter Sixteen*) to a point at half hull draft. (Figure 10-7) Solving for sail area we find that 740 square feet (68.8 m²) would be the maximum allowed. SA x 30 x 2 x 1.6 = 71,000 and SA = 740 sqft.

Wind pressure can be approximated by the formula:

$$P (lb/ft^2) = .004 \, V2 \, (kt)$$
$$P (kg/m^2) = .0053v2 \, (km/hr)$$

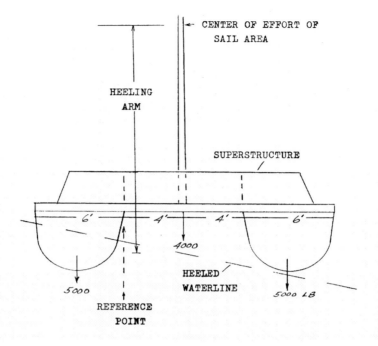

Figure 10-7

An example of measurement of a twenty foot beam sailing catamaran to determine Heeling Arm and Righting Arm.

COMMENTS ON STABILITY

If boats are to carry passengers there are many governmental regulations which must be followed. Each designer must have the rules for the country of operation firmly in place before proceeding with the design. Stability requirements and location of heavy gear may change the entire arrangement plan.

Hull beam is a very important factor for increasing stability in monohulls as the CB is moved further outboard as the hull is immersed, resulting in a larger GZ. But this does not make a case for beamy boats as the hull resistance is also increased with a wider beam. It is a compromise to determine which factor is more important. Sailing craft with centerboards usually have a higher VCG as the ballast is inside the hull and not in a deep keel. For this reason, centerboard sailboats are normally designed with a ten percent wider beam than keelboats.

Figures 10-5 and 10-6 show some curves of righting arms for existing power-boats and sailboats. It is obvious there is little similarity of maximum righting arm (GZ), the angle of heel at maximum GZ and the range of stability. The curves show the importance of calculating the righting arm for every hull and using the area under the curve as an accurate measure of stability.

On figure 10-2 a vertical line is shown through the heeled CB, intersecting the boat centerline at a point called the metacenter (M). The vertical distance from VCG to M is called the metacentric height (GM), which varies with each angle of heel. In past years, this height (GM) was used as an indication of a boat's stability, by comparing one similar boat to another. This measurement has been replaced by the Rahola Criterion in all countries.

HULL FLOODING

The method of finding the stability of a boat has been explained with the assumption the boat is not damaged so water enters the hull. When there is hull damage due to a collision or grounding the stability is seriously impaired because of a change in trim, VCG and displacement. If the entire hull is flooded, only the full flotation described in Chapter Seven will prevent sinking. Complete flooding can be prevented by having many, small watertight compartments.

The construction profile of a powerboat is shown in Figures 11-2 and 11-3 where you can see these watertight spaces. The bulkheads forward and aft of the engines, at the forepeak and under the forward berth are watertight, with watertight doors and hatches. Piping and electrical wiring through these bulkheads must be in watertight fittings. The volume under the aft deck must be watertight to the remainder of the hull.

In addition, the cabin sole (floor) should be watertight at the outboard edges. Flush, watertight hatches can be installed in the floor for access to tank and hull fittings. This will improve the chances of the boat not capsizing or sinking in case of an accident.

SUMMARY

This chapter has shown the method of finding the righting arm (GZ) and the range of stability for any type of hull. Careful attention to the curve of righting arms will show adequate stability or the need to add ballast.

CHAPTER ELEVEN

CONSTRUCTION DRAWINGS

You must have drawings to show the builder just how the boat is constructed. This chapter will show how those drawings are made and what information is displayed. Certainly the experienced builder knows how all the parts go together but he should not assume what is the best procedure for a particular boat.

A SAMPLE CONSTRUCTION DRAWING

Figures 11-1 through 11-6 show the construction drawings for a 44 foot (13.4 m) powerboat. The profile is separated into the forward half and the aft portion only for clarity in this book and it shows glass fiber construction. Despite the difference in shapes, the construction is the same for a sailboat.

In actual practice, the drawings will be covered with notes, explanations and sizes in order to convey all necessary information to the builder. This large amount of lettering is not shown for reasons of clarity. The dimensions and type of material are given for each hull part so there cannot be any interpretation. The method of connecting each part must be exactly stated along with the type of glue or sealant. When manufactured parts or equipment are to be installed, the manufacturer, catalog number and size must be on the drawing. The notes for each part must answer what, where and how.

In the forward half of the example hull, a watertight anchor locker is at the stem with two watertight hatches on deck. Bulkheads divide the accommodations and are usually half inch (13 mm) plywood in boats under 30 ft (9.1 m) and 0.75 in (19 mm) in boats 30 ft (9.1 m) to 45 ft (13.7 m) in length. In metal boats, the bulkheads are normally half the hull bottom thickness and have vertical stiffeners spaced every 20 inches (510 mm), using the same material as the hull. Each bulkhead is watertight to the hull in all boats.

The cabin sole (floor) is the same thickness as the bulkheads, with floor beams spaced 20 inches (510 mm). The outboard edges are watertight to the hull and there are watertight floor hatches wherever necessary. Figure 11-2 shows a small head with the shower just about at the level of the waterline. A pump is shown connected to the shower pan to move the water overboard or to a holding tank. All the pump discharge lines must have a siphon break well above the waterline to prevent accidental siphoning.

VENTILATION IN THE LIVING AREAS

Ventilation is very important as the air inside a hull becomes stale in a few hours and the crew will develop headaches. There are many water trap ventilators on the market and they should be installed wherever they do not interfere with deck operations. An integral water trap vent box can be built at the intersection of the deck and the windshield. This vents the interior on both sides of the boat. Covers can be used under the deck to partially close these vents in cold weather. Be certain to install screens in any opening.

THE ENGINEROOM AREA OF CONSTRUCTION

Figure 11-35 shows the aft portion of the construction profile with commercially available watertight doors at each end of the engineroom. The hull scantlings are usually set for a spacing of about 8 feet (2.44 m) between bulkheads but an engineroom has a concentration of heavy equipment and the transverse (web) frames must be spaced every 30 inches (762 mm). This provides a distribution of weight and stiffening for the tall longitudinal engine girders. These girders extend forward and aft of the engineroom at the height of the cabin sole. Welded steel angles and channels (usually .25 in (6 mm) thick) are fabricated to fit the engine mounts and the top of these girders. The girders are fabricated of 3 in (76 mm) solid glass in a glass hull or hull thickness plate in a metal hull or hull thickness hard wood in a wood hull.

Engine air intake is extremely important in any hull, both to supply air for proper fuel combustion and to remove the engine heat. The air supply should come from the outside of the deck house, above the sheer. The minimum opening in square inches is equal to .33 multiplied by total HP (2.15xtotal HP cm²). If the HP is 300, 100 square inches of vent opening is required. Natural ventilation to the engine is adequate but a continuous duty intake fan is better. The capacity of this fan should be three times the total HP in cuft per minute (.085 HP in m³ / minute). In addition, the same size opening for air to be removed from the engineroom can be located on or above the aft bulkhead. An exhaust fan in this area will assist in reducing the engineroom temperature from the usual 140⁰ F (60⁰ C). Water trap vent boxes with hoses to the engine area make a good installation in sailboats.

The propeller shaft opening is made watertight with a correctly sized stuffing box (shaft seal). This is inspected frequently to insure it is not leaking. In a metal hull, the shaft is inside a heavy pipe welded to the hull. In a wood hull, there is a heavy bronze pipe that is threaded on the outside where it passes through the keel structure. In a glass fiber hull, a glass pipe with .25 in (6 mm) wall is heavily glassed to the hull with a laminate equal to the hull thickness. The stuffing box is connected to the pipe with four stainless steel hose clamps.

A bilge pump is located in each watertight compartment and may be manual or automatic. An exception to this are the small areas under the forward berths that are unused. Some owners prefer a central bilge pumping system in the engineroom with valves (manifold) controlling the flow in pipes to each area of the hull.

Under the aft deck in Figure 11-3, the rudder, shaft tube and shaft strut are shown at the elevation at which they are installed. The rudder is to one side of the propeller shaft centerline, in a twin engine boat, to allow shaft removal without removing the rudder.

A three-armed "Y" strut on the propeller shaft provides the best support for the shaft and good protection for the propeller. The rubber shaft bearing inside the strut is held to the strut by a plastic shell that can be used with all hulls. Do not use a bronze shell with steel or aluminum hulls. The top of the shaft strut is bolted to the hull with an inside backing plate of steel in steel hulls but of aluminum in all other hulls. This backing plate can be 0.25 in (6 mm) in thickness and twice the area of the top of the strut (palm).

EXHAUST SYSTEM

The piping and hose that takes the engine exhaust aft to the outside is called a "wet" exhaust. The sea water (wet) which has cooled the engine's water jacket is put into the exhaust line directly aft of the engine. Many commercial boats have a "dry" exhaust going up from the engine and out a "smoke stack" .Both systems must be air tight to prevent suffocation of the crew with carbon monoxide. Water is not put into the "dry" exhaust and the hot piping must be insulated from its supports and any boat structure it touches.

The "wet" exhaust uses a hose made for exhaust use. It is resistant to high temperatures and sulfuric acid and all joints must be air tight. The gas temperature leaving the engine may be over 800°F (427°C), before the cooling water is injected. The engine exhaust manifold must be the highest point in the exhaust line to prevent sea water from entering the engine. Aluminum or plastic straps with smooth edges are fastened to the deck beams and support the exhaust hose every 24 in (610 mm). A noise muffler is installed just inside the transom.

THE DECK AND DECK HOUSE

The deck plan of the example 44 foot boat is shown in Figure 11-7. Every piece of deck hardware, hatches and ventilators must be in the exact location of installation with reference to the interior bulkheads. The deck plan shows the walking space available and the possible location of equipment to be installed after the boat is built. If an anchor windlass will be installed between the two forward hatches, the cleats will be outboard of the locations shown, just aft of the chocks.

For clarity, the windows in the cabin side (deck house) are not shown. The forward corners of the windshield may be rounded or square, as styling dictates. The radius of the windshield and corners must be stated as well as the exact locations of the house sides and front. If the windows are to be opened, a flat frame will be built, standing out from any radius of the cabin front. The cabin side is raked inboard from the deck as a vertical cabin side looks very clumsy. An upper pilot house should be raked inboard even to a greater degree. A rake of 1:30 in the deck house sides and a rake of 1:10 to the flying bridge or pilot house is common. For engine removal, a water tight hatch may be built into the cabin roof, directly over the floor hatch.

NOTES ON STEEL AND ALUMINUM CONSTRUCTION

Figure 11-5 is a construction section of a steel or aluminum powerboat. A sailboat is built in the same manner. A solid round bar is used at the chine and a heavy pipe forms the rub rail at the sheer. The cabin side framing is extended to the flooring to support the roof. The dashed line to the right shows the path of the fuel vent and fill lines. Metal angles are welded to form a supporting frame for the central engine hatch. This detail may be used with any hull material. In addition, a post is shown in the engineroom to support the center of the engine hatch.

The vertical keel is twice the thickness of the hull bottom and it runs the full length of the boat. It is welded to each transverse frame and to the hull plating. Brackets are welded to the deck and floor beams and to the side frame to support these beams.

NOTES ON WOOD CONSTRUCTION

Figure 11-6 shows a construction section of a typical wood boat. White oak is often used for the keel and frames, with mahogany planking and teak decks. There is a wood rub rail at the sheer which is bolted through the planking and a clamp. The chine is formed of two planks bolted together.

Silicon bronze or stainless steel fastenings are used throughout the hull. Posts on top of the engine girders support the flooring and a centerline post supports the fishing chair. The thickness of the keel is four times the planking thickness and the floor timbers are 1.5 times the thickness of the bottom frames. The outer keel and inner keel are bolted to the horizontal floor timber and the floor timber is bolted to the frames.

SUMMARY

The construction drawings, plan, profile and section have been explained in detail. As a result the builder will know exactly how the designer wants the parts to go together. Each set of drawings will show different materials and their size for varying lengths of boats. The technique of presentation of this information is the same for all types of hulls.

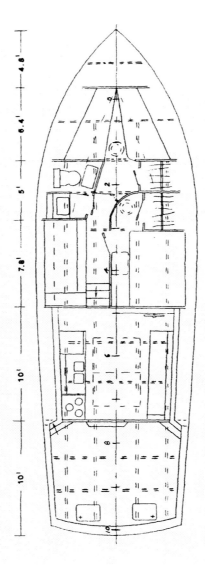

Figure 11-1

Plan view. Bulkheads, hatches and longitudinal girders are shown. On large hulls the bottom framing is drawn on a separate sheet.

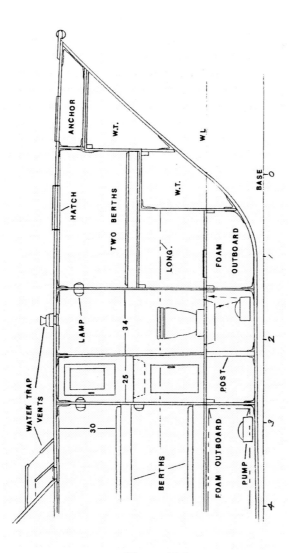

Figure 11-2

Forward half of the construction profile. Watertight sections are shown for-ward and the locations of foam flotation for buoyancy in the event of a collision. The engine girders are extended forward at the height of the cabin sole.

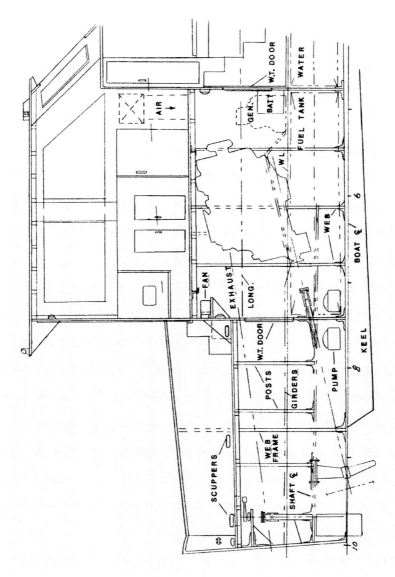

Figure 11-3

Aft portion of the profile. Note the watertight doors at the engineroom.

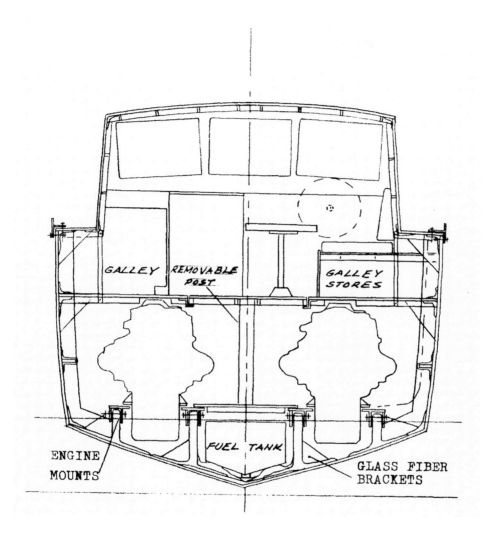

Figure 11-4

Construction section. Note the engine mounts and the brackets supporting the engine girders.

Figures 11-1 to 11-4 all relate to the construction of a 44 foot glass fiber powerboat.

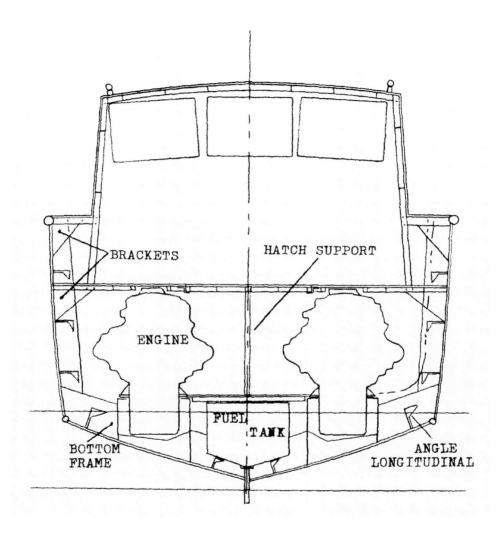

Figure 11-5

Construction of a steel or aluminum powerboat. Note the frame cutouts for the angle longitudinals. The bottom frame is cut away only in the area of the engine oil pan. The engine girders are flanged plate and extend forward and aft at the height of the cabin sole.

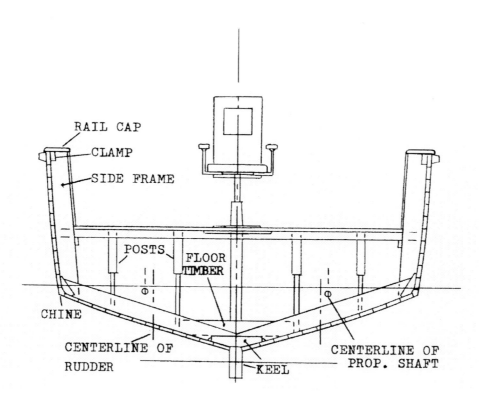

Figure 11-6

Construction section of a wood powerboat showing posts supporting the floor of the fishing cockpit and the fighting chair. The rudder post is set three inches inboard of the propeller shaft for ease of removal.

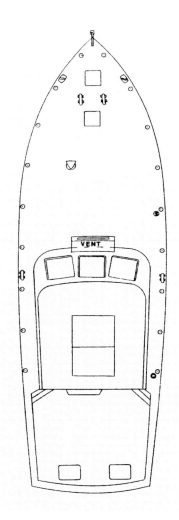

Figure 11-7

Deck plan. Hatches, chocks, cleats, stanchions, water fill, fuel fill and anchor rollers are shown. A tender with davits can be stowed forward of the windshield. Fenders, dock lines, lifejackets, etc. are stowed in small lockers under the cap rail on the aft deck.

CHAPTER TWELVE

CONSTRUCTION DETAILS FOR MULTIHULLS AND SAILBOATS

MULTIHULL CONNECTING BEAMS

The construction of a multihull is the same as a monohull with one giant exception. The deck between the hulls, sometimes called the wing, not only holds the hulls together but it supports the cabin structure. Investigation of the loads on this deck assumes the maximum load occurs in the momentary condition when a large wave passes under the boat and one hull is supported in the crest and the remainder of the boat is unsupported over the trough of the wave. This may occur with both powerboats and sailboats but the latter experiences this condition more frequently when one hull is lifted clear of the water by the wind pressure on the sails. Figures 12-1 and 12-2.

The deck structure acts as a cantilevered beam where the bending moment is taken with reference to the inboard side of the hull in the water. The weight of each hull or superstructure is multiplied by the distance from its center to the reference hull. This bending moment in inch-pounds or m-kg is divided by the allowable stress of the material in pounds per square inch or kPa. The result is the required section modulus for the beams that support the connecting deck. The size of the beams is then found from the section modulus shown in beam tables or by calculation methods found in any textbook on engineering mechanics.

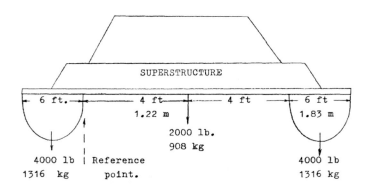

Figure 12-1

Typical catamaran connecting beams for powerboats or sailboats. Bending Moment (BM) = Weight x Length from reference. BM = 2000 (4) + 4000 (11) = 52,000 ft-lb = 624,000 in-lb or 7195 kg-m.

Section Modulus (SM) = BM / S where S = 29,000 psi for glass fiber (199,810 kPa). Use a FS = 2. Required SM = 624,000 (2) / 29,000 = 43 in³ (705 cm³).

If six beams are used, each must have a section modulus equal to 7.16 in³ (117 cm³). Use 7 in x 0.5 in (18 cm x 1.27 cm) flat bars of solid glass fiber under a 0.4 in (1 cm) thick deck of solid glass fiber. Glass ends to hull framing.

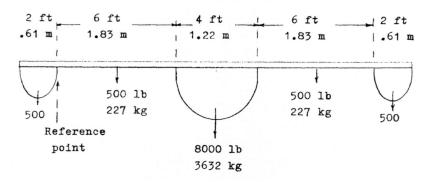

Figure 12-2

Typical trimaran connecting beams for powerboats or sailboats. Bending Moment (BM) = Weight x Length from reference.

BM = 500 (3) + 8000 (8) + 500 (13) + 500 (17) = 80,500 ft-lb = 966,000 in-lb or 11,139 kg-m.

Section Modulus (SM) = BM / S where S = 29,000 psi for glass fiber (199,810 kPa). Use a FS = 2. Required SM = 966,000 (2) / 29,000 = 66.6 in³ (1091 cm³).

If two beams are used, each must have a section modulus equal to 33.3 in³ (546 cm³). Use 8 in x 8 in x 0.5 wall box beams. (20.3 x 20.3 x 1.27 cm wall) Use half inch glass overlay to hull framing. Beams are solid glass.

SAILBOAT MAST STEPS

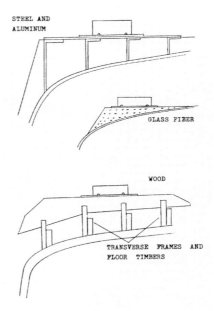

Figure 12-3

Sailboat mast steps

It is important to have a sailboat mast step of sufficient area to distribute the compression load of the mast and to firmly anchor the bottom of the mast. Figure 12-3 shows typical mast steps for wood, metal and glass fiber boats. The mast is provided with a base of aluminum which is sized to fit the shape of the mast. This must be bolted to the structure of the hull bottom. Four or five extra bottom frames are installed in wood and metal boats so their spacing is about 12 inches (305 mm) in the area of the mast. At least two longitudinal frames on both sides of centerline, should span these transverse bottom frames, with the same spacing.

In a glass fiber hull, a platform of solid resin and glass mat can be molded on the hull centerline to support the mast. This platform must be at least 4 in (10 cm) thick and at least 36 inches long (914 mm). A temporary plywood box, lined with wax paper, can be used to mold this platform of resin.

CENTERBOARD PIN INSTALLATION
IN A GLASS FIBER SAILBOAT

Figure 12-4 shows the construction of a centerboard trunk and pin on a glass fiber sailboat. The .75 inch (19 mm) diameter stainless steel pin takes the entire weight of the centerboard. The volume surrounding the pin must be of very solid construction to withstand the racking forces the board places on the hull. The size of the glass fiber at the hull bottom should be at least 12 inches (305 mm) high and 20 inches (914 mm) long. The lead ballast may surround this volume of solid glass. The centerboard should not be any heavier than solid glass to reduce the racking force on the hull.

The width of the centerboard trunk should not be any wider than necessary. This will keep the centerboard on the centerline of the boat. If the centerboard sags to leeward, the ability of the boat to sail to windward will be impaired.

The centerboard trunk should extend well above the waterline so some board area is still in the trunk when the board is completely down. This allows more board area to rest against the trunk and it distributes the load of the water pressure against the board. A watertight inspection plate at the top of the trunk (above the waterline) is helpful to free any debris that may lodge between the board and the trunk. A few ounces of non-polluting vegetable oil poured into the trunk after launching will prevent barnacles from forming inside the trunk. The oil floats on the water and will not wash out. At the next hauling out, the oil will still be floating inside the trunk.

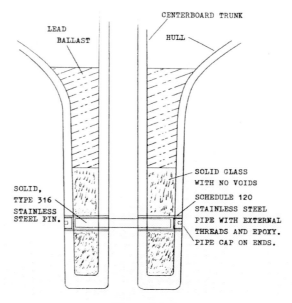

Figure 12-4

Centerboard pin installation in a glass fiber hull.

SAILBOAT CHAINPLATES

The chainplates are bronze or stainless steel straps that secure the wire rigging to the hull. A typical installation is shown on Figure 12-5. On a glass fiber hull, the deck is heavily glassed to the hull so the load is widely distributed. In a steel or aluminum hull, the chainplates are welded to extra hull framing. The thickness of each chainplate is the same as the wire rigging diameter to which it is attached. Each chainplate has a hole for the chainplate pin and the distance from the top of this hole to the top of the chainplate must be twice the wire diameter. See Figure 12-5.

At the stem, a padeye can be used for the jib tack instead of a second chainplate but it must use four bolts and a backing plate. If a shroud chainplate cannot be bolted to a bulkhead, it can have four bolts through a knee, heavily glassed (or welded) to both the deck and the hull and to extra hull framing. The minimum diameter of the four bolts is the diameter of the wire rigging that is supported. Lock washers should be used at each bolt.

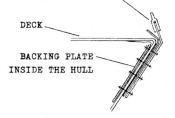

TWO CHAINPLATES AT STEM FOR HEADSTAY
AND JIB TACK, BOLTED THROUGH THE HULL.

DECK

BACKING PLATE
INSIDE THE HULL

X DISTANCE EQUALS TWICE THE WIRE RIGGING DIAMETER.

CHAINPLATE FOR A SHROUD

COVER PLATE AT DECK WITH
BEDDING COMPOUND

BACKING PLATE

BOLTS (4)

GLASS FIBER KNEE
HEAVILY GLASSED TO
HULL AND DECK.
WELDED CONSTRUCTION
IS SIMILAR.

Figure 12-5

Sailboat chainplates

A DEEP BALLAST KEEL IN A SAILBOAT

Racing sailboats now use all the ballast in a torpedo shaped bulb. This is connected to the hull by a narrow and thin keel (fin keel) which assures the ballast is as low as the boat draft will permit. The stress on this fin keel and the hull structure must be carefully investigated to insure there is adequate support. Calculations will be shown for a glass fiber hull but a welded fin keel uses the same procedure.

When the sailboat heels, a large bending moment occurs in the fin keel just at the bottom of the hull. This is resisted by the transverse (web) frames inside the hull and by the section modulus (SM) of the fin keel. Figure 12-6 and assumes the total keel weight is 6000 lbs (2720 kg) with the total center of gravity ten feet (3.05

m) from the hull bottom. The resulting bending moment (BM) is 60,000 ft-lb (8300 kg-m) at the hull bottom. The hull, keel and framing are solid glass with an allowable bending strength of 29,000 psi (199,810 kPa). The required section modulus is BM / S. (SM = BM divided by S)

$$SM = 60,000 \ (12) \ FS. \ 6 \ / \ 29,000 = 149 \ in^3 \ (2442 \ cm^3)$$

The fin keel is assumed to be an ellipse in sectional shape, where the section modulus (SM) = pi (1) w^2 / 32. Other shapes must be calculated. Use a length of 48 in (127 cm) and a width of 6 in (16 cm) where the keel SM is: (pi=3.1416)

$$SM = 3.14 \times 48 \times 36 \ / \ 32 = 170 \ in^3 \ (2780 \ cm^3),$$ which is greater than required and is satisfactory. Inside the hull, the transverse frames should be a minimum of 12 in (30.5 cm) high, with at least three frames forward and aft of the keel centerline. The total compression load on the top of the frames is 6000 lb (2720 kg) which is transmitted by a stainless steel bar resting on one transverse frame. The allowable compression stress on a glass fiber laminate averages 10,000 psi (68,900 kPa). Use a factor of safety of six with this stress. The required bearing area is 6000 x 6 / 10,000 = 3.6 in² (23 cm²).

A 12 in (30.5 cm) long bar glassed to a solid glass frame of one inch (2.54 cm) thickness is satisfactory.

The transverse frames also resist the bending moment of the fin keel. This load is 60,000 ft-lb (8300 kg-m) at the top of the one foot (.305 m) high transverse frame. The resulting compression load on the frame is 60,000 lb (27,250 kg). Dividing by the allowable compression stress and multiplying by a factor of safety of six, the required bearing area is (Glass fiber):

$$60,000 \times 6 \ / \ 10,000 = 36 \ in^2 \ (232 \ cm^2)$$

Each transverse frame provides 12 sq. in (77 cm²) of bearing area, so there must be a minimum of three transverse frames heavily glassed to the side of the solid glass fin keel.

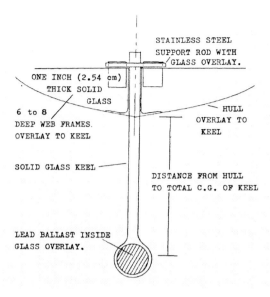

STAINLESS STEEL
SUPPORT ROD WITH
GLASS OVERLAY.

ONE INCH (2.54 cm)
THICK SOLID
GLASS

6 to 8
DEEP WEB FRAMES.
OVERLAY TO KEEL

HULL
OVERLAY TO
KEEL

SOLID GLASS KEEL

DISTANCE FROM HULL
TO TOTAL C.G. OF KEEL

LEAD BALLAST INSIDE
GLASS OVERLAY.

Figure 12-6

Hull support for a deep keel. The fin keel is centered longitudinally on the center of gravity of the ballast.

SUMMARY

This chapter has discussed a few important construction details concerning multihull connecting beams, sailboat chainplates, mast steps, centerboards and fin keels. All of these subjects are vital to the successful operation of the boat and are sometimes not given sufficient attention. The method of construction applies to any type of hull built with any material.

CHAPTER THIRTEEN

ENGINEROOM EQUIPMENT, STEERING AND RUDDERS

It is important to understand what equipment is put in the engineroom so space is used efficiently to provide access to each item. In large, cruising power-boats, about one-third of the total boat cost is concentrated in the engineroom. This cost seems to increase as boat owners demand more equipment to provide all the comforts of home. This chapter will discuss the arrangement of the engineroom, the types of steering systems and the calculations for the size of rudders.

ENGINEROOM ARRANGEMENT

Figure 13-1 shows a typical engineroom arrangement with watertight doors at each end. The length of the engine space may be just the engine length in a small sailboat without a generator or hot water heater but a large powerboat usually has an engineroom length of twice the length of the engine installed.

The dimensions of each item are carefully drawn on the engineroom plan to allow easy access for routine maintenance. The engine exhausts from each side of a "V" block engine are brought together in a collector box before exiting aft. These exhausts are high in the engineroom to provide positive drainage aft. Other equipment can be located under these exhausts, on both sides of the propeller shaft. All installed equipment must be balanced port and starboard so the boat remains in level trim.

Photo 13

Joinerwork installed around this sailboat's engine compartment will conceal the engine and provide reasonable access to the engine.

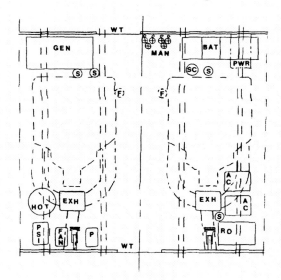

Figure 13-1

Engineroom plan: AC-Air Conditioning, BAT-Batteries, EXH-Collector for engine exhaust, F-Fuel filters, FAN-Air exhaust fan, GEN-Genset, HOT-Hot water tank, MAN-Manifold for fuel and water valves, P-Bilge pump, PSI-pressure water pump, PWR-Shore power breaker, RO-Water maker, SC-Sea water chest, S-Sea water strainer, WT-Watertight doors.

SALT WATER SEA CHEST

Sea water is required for the cooling of the engines, generator, air conditioning condenser and the watermaker. Instead of separate fittings through the hull, it is more efficient to have one large pipe (sea chest) entering the hull and extending well above the waterline. There is a removable pipe cap on top of the sea chest pipe for inspection and cleaning. Individual, smaller pipes are welded (glassed) to the side of the sea chest for each piece of equipment. If flexible hoses are used from the sea chest to the strainers, there must be two stainless steel hose clamps at each end.

In an aluminum or steel hull, the sea chest is welded and four brackets are installed between the pipe and the hull, to half height. In a glass fiber hull, a half-inch (13 mm) wall glass fiber pipe is installed with the overlay to the hull equal to the hull thickness. In addition, four glass fiber brackets are installed to half height.

Photo 5

This sailboat has a sea chest (black vertical pipe) located next to the white mast. The top of the sea chest is eight inches above the heeled waterline with a pipe cap to ease cleaning. The sea water used for cooling the engine and genset run from this sea chest to the units. Notice the hoses only have one clamp each. Two clamps should be used on each hose as clamp failure is the most common reason for sinking.

STEERING

The choices for steering for small boats are many but boats over forty feet (12.2 m) generally use a hydraulic system, especially when there is more than one helm station. Because of light weight and low cost, many small sailboats use a tiller directly connected to the rudder. If the helm is near the rudder in a small boat, a push-pull type of cable or cable and sheave system is often used. There are many steering systems on the market and most can be used with an autopilot. Whatever the system, the manufacturer's installation instructions must be carefully followed.

The helm, should be located on the boat's centerline or to starboard so the person steering can be more aware of any other vessels to starboard. This has been a ruling in court cases after an accident as the rules for navigation state that any vessel to starboard has the right of way.

Photo 6

Rudder post detail in a glass fiber sailboat. Below the steering cable is a steel channel to support the weight of the rudder, post and steering sheave (quadrant).

RUDDER CONSTRUCTION

The shaft attached to the rudder blade is commonly called the rudder post and it is usually of stainless steel. The rudder blade can be cast bronze except on a metal hull or it can be built up of glass fiber, steel or aluminum. In the latter case, a plate is welded to the post for primary support and the external rudder shape is fabricated around this plate on the rudder centerline.

The weight of the rudder is taken by a foundation built inside the hull and secured to the transom and hull bottom. The hull material is used for this foundation. A collar on this foundation is bolted through the rudder post and it turns on a washer plate of stainless steel. There is a stuffing box below the foundation to keep the water out and a tiller arm or quadrant is secured above the foundation.

Photo 4

Shaft strut, supported rudder and protecting keel on a rugged aluminum work boat.

RUDDER FORCE

The turning force (torque) on the rudder is caused by the water force on the blade. This must be found in order to select the right size steering gear. Figure 13-4, Rudder Areas, has been developed from the experience of many designs.

The torque on the rudder post (shaft) is entirely twisting (torsion) due to the water force on the rudder blade if the bottom of the rudder is supported. If the rudder post is not supported (spade rudder), it is also subject to bending at the hull bottom. Both types will be investigated and sample calculations made.

RUDDER AREAS			
Powerboats: Area = .08 LWL (ft) or .024 LWL (m)			
LWL feet	Area sqft	LWL meters	Area sq meters
20	1.6	6.1	0.15
30	2.4	9.1	0.22
40	3.2	12.2	0.29
50	4	15.2	0.37
60	4.8	18.3	0.45
70	5.6	21.3	0.52
80	6.4	24.4	0.59
90	7.2	27.4	0.66
Sailboats: Area = .007 L^2 (ft) or (m)			
20	2.8	6.1	0.26
30	6.3	9.1	0.58
40	11.2	12.2	1.04
50	17.5	15.2	1.62
60	25.2	18.2	2.34

Figure 13-4

Note on powerboats. The rudder height is measured from the hull down to a point 0.8 depth of the propeller. The rudder width is about 0.6 multiplied by the rudder height.

Supported Rudders: (Figure 13 - 2)

The torque on the supported rudder post is the product of the sine of 45 degrees rudder angle (.707); rudder area (A); the moment arm (L) from the center of the area to the rudder post centerline; the square of the boat speed (V^2); the density of sea water; and all divided by the acceleration due to gravity. The sine of an angle is a term in geometry defined as the side of a triangle opposite the subject angle, divided by the hypotenuse (longest side) of the triangle. For an angle of 45 degrees, the sine equals .707. Refer to an engineering handbook for more information.

Torque $= ALV^2 (.707)$ 64 lb/ft^3 / 32.18 ft/sec^2.

If V^2 is in knots, multiply by 2.85 to get ft^2/sec^2 and multiply by 12 inches in a foot to get lb-in. Combining the above, Torque = 48 ALV^2 lb-in with A in sqft, L in feet and V in knots. In the SI system, V is in km/hour, A in m^2 and L in meters.

Torque $= ALV^2 (.707)$ 1025 kg/m^3 / (3600^2 x 9.8 m/sec^2)
Torque $= 5.706$ ALV^2 kg-m.

An example of the rudder TORQUE calculation uses a rudder area (A) of three square feet; a distance of 0.75 feet from the center of the rudder area to the rudder post (L); and a boat speed (V) of fifteen knots. TORQUE equals 48 ALV^2 (from above) pound-inches.

T = 48 (3) (0.75) 225
T = 24,300 pound-inches, for a supported rudder.

The torsional resisting moment of a solid, circular shaft is pi x d^3 / 16 multiplied by the materials allowable stress. The yield stress in torsion of common stainless steel is 20,000 psi (137,800 kPa) (14.1 x 10^6 kg/m^2). Combining the above and equating to the torque, we have:

(pi is a mathematical constant equal to 3.1416)
d^3 = pi x 20,000 / 16 (FS. 1.4) = 48 ALV^2 lb-in
d^3 = 1075.2 ALV^2 / 62,832 = 0.0171 ALV^2 in^3 in SI-
d^3 = pi x 14.1 x 10^6 / 16 (FS. 1.4) = 5.706 ALV^2 kg-m
d^3 = 127.8 ALV^2 / 44.3 x 10^6 = 2.885 x 10^{-6} ALV^2 m^3
d^3 = 2885 ALV^2 mm^3 (solid rudder post diameter)^3

For example, we consider a supported rudder area (A) of three square feet; a distance from the center of the rudder area to the rudder post of 0.75 feet (L); and a boat speed of 15 knots (V). The diameter of the rudder post is:

d³ equals .0171 multiplied by Area, multiplied by distance to rudder post, multiplied by the square of the boat speed in knots.

$$d^3 = .0171 \ ALV^2 \ (in^3)$$
$$d^3 = .0171 \ (3) \ (0.75) \ 225$$
$$d^3 = 8.657 \text{ and the rudder post diameter is two inches. } (2.05)$$

DIAMETER OF SUPPORTED SOLID RUDDER POST - INCHES/MM							
RUDDER AREA	BOAT SPEED IN KNOTS/KM PER HOUR						
SQ FT M²	5/9.3	10/18.5	15/27.8	20/37.1	30/55.6	40/74.2	50/92.7
2	0.19	.78/20	1.25/32	1.63/41	2/51	2.6/66	3.14/80	3.5/89
3	0.28	.97/25	1.53/39	2/51	2.43/62	3.2/81	3.9/99	4.5/114
4	0.37	1.11/28	1.76/45	2.3/59	2.8/71	3.66/93	4.43/113	5.15/131
6	0.56	1.34/34	2.2/56	2.9/74	3.5/89	4.5/115	5.5/140	6.4/163
8	0.74	1.58/40	2.5/64	3.3/84	4/102	5.2/132	6.3/160	7.3/185
10	0.93	1.77/45	2.8/71	3.7/94	4.45/113	5.85/149	7.1/180	8.2/208
12	1.11	1.92/49	3.1/79	4/102	4.85/123	6.35/161	7.7/196	8.9/226
18	1.67	2.36/60	3.76/96	4.9/125	5.9/150	7.8/197	9.4/239	11/280

Figure 13-2

Height of rudder is assumed to be 1.5 width. Other shapes must be calculated. Material yield in torsion assumed at 20,000 psi (137,800 kPa). This chart is only for supported rudders and must not be used with spade rudders.

Photo 17   John P. Kaufman

Photo 16   John P. Kaufman

Photo 17 shows a planning hull powerboat with spade rudders (not support). Photo 16 shows a full keel cruising sailboat with the rudder supported.

<u>Spade Rudders (Not Supported)</u>: (Figure 13 - 3)

The torque for twisting is calculated in the above manner and the torque for bending (Tb) is calculated in a like manner but using the arm for bending (L) from the center of the rudder area to the bottom of the hull. The two values of torque are combined using a standard engineering formula:

Total Torque = Tb / 2 + ((Tb / 2)^2 + T^2)$^{.5}$

The total torque is then equated to d^{3}pi / 16 multiplied by the torsional stress of the material, as above and the equation solved for the post diameter.

For example, considering a solid shaft where the rudder area (A) is 6 sqft (.557m), twisting arm is one foot (.305 m), bending arm is 1.5 ft (.458 m) and the boat speed (V) is 30 knots (55.62 km/hr):

Torque (twisting) = 48 ALV^2 (5.706 ALV^2)
T = 48 (6) 1 (900) = 259,200 lb-in
T = 5.706 (.557) .305 (3094) = 2999 kg-m
Torque (bending) Tb = 48 ALV^2 (5.706 ALV^2)
Tb = 48 (6) 1.5 (900) = 388,800 lb-in
Tb = 5.706 (.557) .458 (3094) = 4504 kg-m
Total torque = 194,400 + ((194,400)^2 + (259,200)^2)$^{0.5}$ = 194,400 + 323,800 = 518,200 lb-in
Total torque = 2252 + (2252^2 + 2999^2)$^{0.5}$ = 2252 + 3750 = 6002 kg-m

The rudder post diameter is found as follows:

d^3 (pi) 20,000 psi / 16 (F.S.1.4) = Torque of 518,200
d^3 = 184.74 in^3 and d = 5.7 inches (See figure 13-3)
d^3 (pi) 14.1 x 10^6 / 16 (FS 1.4) = Torque of 6002 kg-m
d^3 = 3035.1 x 10^{-6} m^3 or 3,035,100 mm^3; d = 144.79 mm

Figures 13-2 and 13-3 show the rudder post diameters for supported rudders and spade rudders.

If a hollow rudder post is desired in order to save weight, the following formula is used to convert from a solid shaft:

D^3 = (od^4-id^4) / od where D = solid shaft diameter, od = outside diameter of hollow shaft and id = inside diameter of hollow shaft.

For example, if we wanted to replace a two inch diameter solid shaft, we could use a hollow shaft with an outside diameter of 2.5 inches and an inside diameter (id) of 2.05 inches.

D^3 = (od^4 - id^4) divided by the od.

$D^3 = (39.06 - 17.66)$ divided by 2.5
$D^3 = 8.56$ and the solid diameter is 2.0456 inches.

Since this is greater than 2.0 inches, the selected hollow shaft can replace the two inch diameter solid shaft. The hollow shaft would weigh much less than the solid shaft.

Most manufactured rudders with posts have some rudder area projecting forward of the post (balance). This area should be kept to a minimum. Any area forward of the rudder post is subject to the force of water moving aft and thus helps to turn the rudder, reducing the load on the steering gear. But the drag is also increased and balance is not recommended on either sailboats or powerboats.

DIAMETER OF SPADE SOLID RUDDER POST - INCHES/MM								
RUDDER AREA		BOAT SPEED IN KNOTS/KM PER HOUR						
SQ FT	M²	5/9.3	10/18.5	15/27.8	20/37.1	30/55.6	40/74.2	50/92.7
2	0.19	1/25	1.58/40	2/51	2.51/64	3.30/84	4/102	4.62/117
3	0.28	1.22/31	2/51	2.53/64	3.1/79	4/102	4.9/125	5.65/144
4	0.37	1.41/36	2.24/57	2.93/74	3.55/90	4.65/118	5.64/143	6.54/166
6	0.56	1.72/44	2.74/70	3.6/92	4.34/110	5.7/145	6.9/175	8/204
8	0.74	2/51	3.16/80	4.14/105	5/127	6.55/167	7.97/202	9.24/234
10	0.93	2.22/56	3.52/90	4.63/118	5.6/142	7.34/187	8.9/226	10.3/260
12	1.11	2.44/62	3.86/98	5.07/129	6.14/156	8.05/205	9.75/248	11.3/288
18	1.67	3/76	4.75/121	6.22/158	7.54/192	9.9/251	12/305	13.9/353

Figure 13-3

Height of rudder is assumed to be 1.5 width. Other shapes must be calculated. Material yield in torsion assumed at 20,000 psi (137,800 kPa).

SUMMARY

This chapter discussed engineroom arrangement, rudder size and the calculation of rudder force for both spade and supported rudders. These construction details are extremely important to the success of the boat's operation.

CHAPTER FOURTEEN

TANKS AND PIPING

The installation of the tanks and associated piping is of prime importance to the boat owner as it is intended to be correct and permanent. After the boat is completed, it is very difficult to remove tanks or piping for any repairs, so the job must be done correctly the first time. Not only must the fuel or water system be watertight but it must withstand any vibration or impact loads transmitted by the hull.

TANKS

Fuel, water and waste tanks may be of different materials in different hulls but generally fuel tanks are aluminum and water tanks are stainless steel. There are some plastic tanks on the market for water but some of these tanks have not been of the best quality. Steel and aluminum hulls may use separate tanks of the same material as the hull or they may use integral tanks where one side of the tank is the side of the hull. Integral tanks may not be used on glass fiber hulls as the glass overlay at the edges may break loose as the hull flexes. Steel tanks must be painted on the outside to prevent rusting. Steel or aluminum water tanks must be painted on the inside with a paint formulated for potable water, to prevent an odd taste in the water.

All tanks should be tested to 5 psi (34.5 kPa). All tanks should be built to the U.S. Coast Guard requirements for small passenger vessels (CG-323). Tanks in large hulls may have to be tested to more than 5 psi (11 feet (3.4 m) of static head) as overfilling may put a higher pressure on the tank. This occurs when the fill and vent piping is more than 11 ft (5.4 m) from the bottom of the tank.

Tanks are often located in the hull bottom, just on top of the frames, so the center of gravity is as low as possible. When there is not sufficient space in the bilge for all the fuel required, the tanks are often installed outboard against the side of the hull. These tanks may extend from the bilge to the deck, leaving room near the boat centerline for a walkway and other equipment. It is poor practice to install piping or electrical wiring outboard of these tanks, just inside the hull.

Large boats often have every area of the bilge used for tanks, with the top of a tank forming the cabin flooring in a metal boat with integral tanks. This is poor practice as the weight of all the interior joinerwork is resting on the tanks. It is better practice to have tanks port and starboard with vertical posts on the boat centerline to support floor beams that take the weight of the interior.

The longitudinal location of tanks should be close to the boat's center of gravity so the trim is not affected when the tanks are completely full or empty. If the tanks are at the stern, the boat will be down by the stern when the tanks are full and the boat will run poorly, even with high installed horsepower.

Diesel fuel is pumped to the engine fuel pump in much greater volume than is used by the engine injectors and most of this diesel fuel is returned to the tank. The temperature of this returned fuel is over 100 degrees F (37.8 C) and if the fuel tank is under a berth, the stateroom can become excessively warm. Insulation around the tank will normally correct this problem.

One, or more, tanks are used for each engine to allow fuel to be delivered to any engine in the event one tank is contaminated. Boats over 36 feet (11 m) have two or more water tanks for the same reason. The electrical generators usually have their own fuel tank as they run on a different time schedule than the engines.

A sketch of the fuel system piping is shown in Figure 14-1 where each tank can deliver fuel to any engine and each engine may return fuel to any tank. The fuel transfer pump moves fuel from one tank to another. The stop valves isolate one engine and one tank from the others. These valves are located in the engineroom, grouped together in a "manifold".

Tanks can be on either side of the hull but should not extend from port to starboard. The latter condition allows the tank liquid to flow from side to side, with the roll of the boat. This increases the roll and makes the boat uncomfortable if not dangerous.

All tanks must have baffles spaced not more than 20 inches (51cm) apart to stiffen the sides of the tank. If the tank is more than three feet (0.9 m) in height, there must be additional horizontal stiffeners located either inside or outside the tank. The vertical baffles inside the tank have a large hole in the center and the four corners are sniped to allow the liquid slow movement throughout the tank.

The thickness of the tank material may be calculated in a similar manner as the hull thickness. The test pressure, 5 psi (34.5 kPa) or greater, is used with the baffle spacing of 20 inches (51cm) and the allowable yield or bending strength of the tank material. Using an aluminum tank as an example:

$$t^2 = P \, l^2 / 2S$$
$$t^2 = 5 \, (400) / 2 \, (18000) = 0.0555 \text{ and } t = .236 \text{ in (6 mm)}.$$

On the top of each tank there should be a 6 inch (15.2 cm) watertight inspection plate for inspection and cleaning. There will be no fittings or openings on the bottom of the tank as a leak would allow the entire contents of the tank to flood the hull.

PIPING

Fuel and water piping may be copper, seamless steel, copper - nickel or aluminum with fittings which are galvanically compatible. Plastic pipe is only used on small, less expensive hulls and only for water or waste. Fittings on plastic tanks should not be secured with adhesives. All fittings should be threaded in a normal manner and made of bronze, steel or aluminum.

Bilge pumps are normally submersible electric pumps with an integral suction and a hose discharge. This discharge is often combined with a sink drain line in order to minimize the through hull valves. It is always better to use solid piping instead of a flexible hose as the two hose clamps at each end may loosen or deteriorate.

In large hulls, a central, engine driven bilge pump may be located in the engineroom with plastic or metal piping to each watertight compartment. Normally, there is a "manifold" of stop/check valves near the central bilge pump, with one valve in each of the bilge suction lines. At the suction end of each line there is a strainer to prevent debris from clogging the pump.

Piping of any type should not run inside an integral tank. Usually, all piping is located under the flooring (cabin sole) and is held in place with metal or plastic straps bolted to the floor beams. If metal, these straps must have smooth edges and a lining of plastic or rubber in contact with the pipe. A a hangar is shown in 14 - 2.

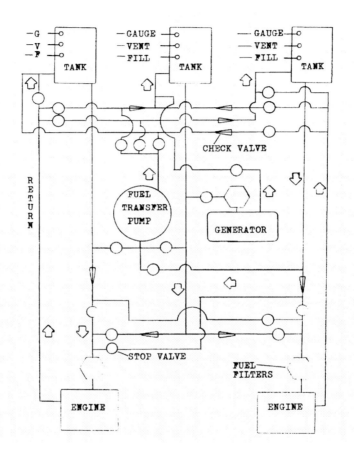

Figure 14-1

Diesel fuel piping system. In normal operation, each engine would be supplied from one tank.

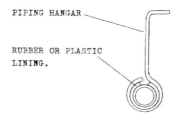

PIPING HANGAR

RUBBER OR PLASTIC
LINING.

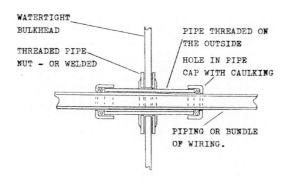

WATERTIGHT
BULKHEAD

THREADED PIPE
NUT - OR WELDED

PIPE THREADED ON
THE OUTSIDE

HOLE IN PIPE
CAP WITH CAULKING

PIPING OR BUNDLE
OF WIRING.

Figure 14-2

Piping System

Vibration and shock loads contribute to fatigue failure of piping and it is essential pipe hangars be located not more than 39 inches (1 m) apart. Hangars for exhaust piping should be half that distance apart. Piping hangars should not be less than one inch (25 mm) in width and the thickness can be calculated to withstand a load of 500 lbs (227 kg). In the case of an aluminum hangar one inch (25 mm) in width, we use a factor of safety of two with the yield strength of 18000 psi (124020 kPa). Therefore, 500 / 9000 x 1 = .056 in (1.4 mm). 124020 kPa / 98 = 1265.5 kg/cm^2 and 227 kg / 632.75 x 2.54 = 0.14 cm thickness.

In the engineroom, piping should be rigid rather than hose with hose clamps, if possible. Hose clamps have a tendency to loosen. An exception to this are the fuel lines at the engines. A flexible section of fuel hose, with flare fitting connections, is used so the vibration of the engine will not affect the piping. Through hull fittings and valves should have brackets to the hull as the valves may be stepped on by careless workers. The sea water to the engines passes through sea water strainers and the size of the piping should be the same as the strainer fittings. The only size reducing fitting allowed, if necessary, is at the engine. If reducing pipe fittings are used ahead of the strainers, they may trap grass and mud which would stop the water flow and overheat the engine.

As the piping passes through watertight bulkheads, it must be watertight. One example is shown on Figure 14-2.

SUMMARY

The best quality tanks and piping are essential to the continuous, safe operation of the boat. This chapter has shown how the tanks and piping are assembled in the hull.

CHAPTER FIFTEEN

SAIL PLANS AND MASTS

Part I   THE SAIL PLAN

Many different types of sails have been used in the past 2000 years and the few currently used are a matter of owner preference. All must have a total area sufficient to move the boat in ten knots of wind. The center of the total area (Center of Effort - CE) must be in a location that results in a slight but not strong, tendency for the hull to turn into the wind (weather helm). We will investigate the various rig types and solve the above requirements.

Ancient boats used a square sail or a triangular sail set on a short mast with a rotating luff spar (sprit or gaff) similar to the Mediterranean felucca. This sail is sometimes called a lateen sail. The triangular sail has evolved to what is called a jib-headed or Bermudian sail which is the most popular. A specialization of this sail is the omnipresent type of wind surfer. A boat with a single sail is often called a "cat boat", although the original type of cat boat had a quadrilateral sail with a gaff at the top (gaff headed).

Square sails were low aspect ratio rectangles that were only efficient when the wind was aft of the beam. The ship could only tack through 180 degrees on the compass where modern rigs can tack through 90 degrees on the compass from port to starboard tack. Square rigged ships were used primarily in the "trade winds" areas of the world where the course from port to port had the prevailing wind aft of the beam.

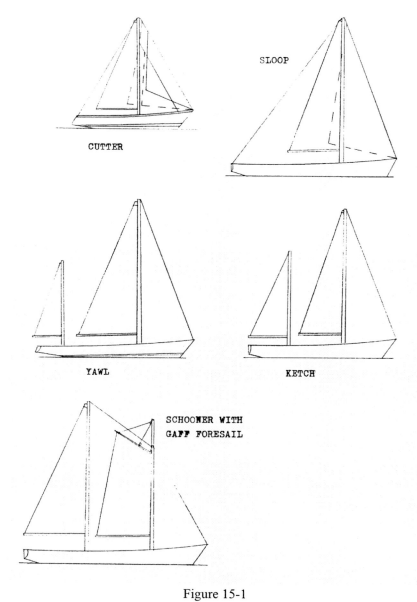

Figure 15-1

Types of sail plans.

SLOOPS & CUTTERS

A sloop rig has one mast with a mainsail and jib and the mast is about 28% to 35% of the length on deck aft of the bow. A cutter has one mast about 35% to 40 % of the deck length aft of the bow. The cutter usually has a jibstay aft of the headstay so two jibs can be used. Tall masts with short booms (high aspect ratio) have proven to be the most efficient but at higher cost. Various staysails and spinnakers are used for racing and sometimes in light air on cruising boats, limited only by the imagination of the sailmaker. (Figure 16 - 1)

YAWLS AND KETCHES

These boats have a shorter mizzen mast and sail aft of the mainmast and its location determines the proper name. If the mizzen mast is forward of the rudder post, the boat is a ketch and if aft, a yawl. Most modern boats have short overhangs (distance from the end of the waterline to the stern or bow) and the rudder post is almost at the stern. Thus, most new hulls with mizzen masts are ketches. To be effective, the mizzen sail should be at least 30% of the mainsail area. The advantage of a yawl or ketch is the ability to furl the mainsail in strong winds and proceed with the mizzen and small jib and have normal balance to the helm. A mizzen staysail can be set in moderate winds when the apparent wind is abeam and aft on the quarter.

SCHOONERS

A schooner also has two masts with the forward mast (foremast) shorter or the same height as the mainmast. The foresail and mainsail may be jib-headed or gaff rigged and sometimes a staysail is carried between the masts. Various combinations of sails are used to get the maximum sail area in light winds, which is the objective with any type of rig.

WINGSAILS

Many fine attempts have been made to increase the efficiency of the traditional fabric sail as it has long been recognized that poor results are obtained when the sail sits in the wind shadow of the mast. Designing a mast integrated with the sail has resulted in the wingsail which has proven to be very efficient. A great deal of credit is due the designers of the class "C" catamarans, both in England and the USA, who have developed the wingsail in various forms. These sails consist of two or three vertical sections of airfoils that are rotated to achieve a shape similar to an aircraft wing. This shape has a definite high and low pressure surface to achieve lifting forces. These wingsails were rigid structures that had to be removed from the boat each evening and this negated their popularity for use in average hulls. Among the many wingsails that have been developed in recent years, two will be briefly mentioned.

WALKER WINGSAIL SYSTEMS PLC

John Walker of Plymouth, England has patented a rigid wingsail system that uses one or more thrust foils with the forward half of each foil always pointed into the wind. These forward sections are rigidly connected to a foil mounted aft that keeps the forward half of the thrust foils pointed to windward. The aft portion of each thrust foil (wing) is rotated by electric motor so the sectional shape of each thrust foil is similar to an aircraft wing. All the foils are mounted on a rotating platform together with a trimaran hull. All the foils are pointed into the wind at the dock and in very heavy winds, as they are rigid structures. A windmill generator or solar panel provides the electricity. One of their 54 foot (16.5 m) trimarans with Walker Wingsails has cruised over 15,000 miles (27810 km) including a successful cruise to the USA and return to England. Figure 16 - 2, Planesail Yachts.

COMSAIL CO. LTD

Jack Manners-Spencer of Lymington, England has patented a wingsail made of rigid battens and two sides of sailcloth. These battens and sailcloth slide vertically over a rigid mast entirely contained within the battens and sailcloth. The side view and sectional shape is that of a symmetrical aircraft wing. The wingsail is raised and lowered to any height for reefing and is lowered completely, in the normal manner, for furling.

The mast can be made from any material but is usually fabricated from unidirectional glass fiber or other composite plastic. All the loading on the mast is in bending as there is no rigging wire. Over fifty cruising sailboats are using these wingsails in various ports of the world.

The advantage of all the wingsails is one person can handle the boat. There are no sails to change and there are no extra sails to carry.

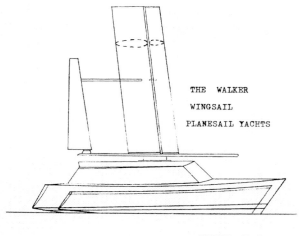

THE WALKER

WINGSAIL

PLANESAIL YACHTS

FIGURE 15-2

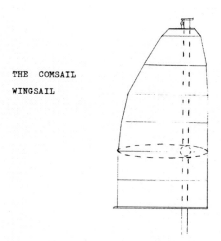

THE COMSAIL

WINGSAIL

Figure 15-2

Walker and Comsail wingsails.

SAIL AREA REQUIRED

In designing the sail plan, we consider only the basic sails without staysails or spinnakers. The area forward of the mast is considered the height of the mast and length from mast to jibstay (foretriangle) without regard to the size of the jibs that will be used. The size of mainsails, mizzens and foresails is used exactly. (Figure 16-3)

The determination of the correct amount of sail area is open to question as we expect to reef when the wind force is about 16 knots (30 km/hr) but we also want all the sail area we can find in winds less than 10 knots (18.5 km/hr). Experience has shown the ratio of sail area divided by displacement (cubic feet or cubic meters) to the 0.667 power provides a good indicator of required sail area.

This ratio should be about 16 for cruising sailboats and about 20 for racing sailboats. If we use this ratio with un-ballasted multihulls, it is common to find the sail area ratio to be 25 or more. For example, if we have a boat of 18,000 lbs (6172 kg), this is 281.25 cuft (7.98 cum). Taking the 0.667 power of displacement, we have 42.9 sqft (4 sqm). If the total sail area is 800 sqft (74.4 sqm), the ratio for sail area is 18.6 which is acceptable.

The sail area shown on Figure 16-3 is measured by taking the area of a right triangle which is one-half of the base length multiplied by the height.

The mainsail is 10 ft x 20 ft / 2 which is 100 sqft. The foretriangle is 9 ft. x 22.5 ft / 2 which is 101 sqft. The area of any triangle may be measured by multiplying one-half of the length of the longest side by the perpendicular length (LP) to that longest side.

In Figure 16-3, this is 8.4 ft x 24 ft / 2, which is 101 sqft. If a quadrilateral sail is used, it is divided into two triangles and the area found, as above.

SAIL AREA CENTERS OF EFFORT AND HELM BALANCE

A slight tendency for the boat to head into the wind (weather helm) is necessary to steer a course to windward. This weather helm is dependent on the water forces on the hull shape and the wind forces on the airfoil of each sail. These forces are difficult to describe and there is a simplified method to determine what the balance of the helm will be on a monohull.

The horizontal separation of the centers of effort (CE) of the combined sail plan and the center of lateral plane (CLP) is used to gauge the amount of weather helm. This separation of centers is called "lead" (as in leading a horse) and is expressed as a percentage of the waterline length. In Figure 16-3, the lead is 3.8ft. Dividing by the waterline length of 23.5 feet, we have 16.2%. This is a good value for a cruising, ballasted, sailboat. Racing skippers usually like a lighter weather helm and a lead of 20% is common.

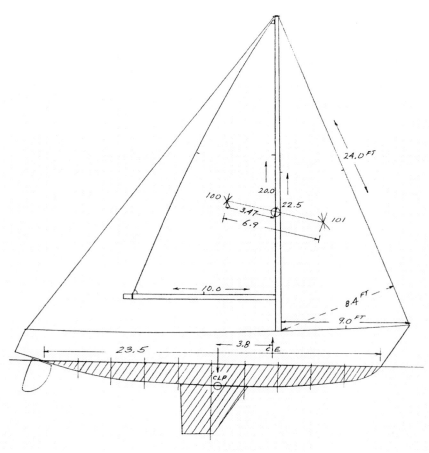

Figure 15-3

Calculation of sail area, centers of effort and center of lateral plane.

The center of effort (CE) of a triangular sail is found by drawing a straight line from each corner to the center of the opposite side. Figure 15-3. These individual CE are combined by using an algebraic formula, The same as calculating weights and distances on a seesaw.

For example, the distance between the two CE on Figure 15-3 is measured at 6.9 feet. The sail area multiplied by the distance to the new, total CE, equals the other sail area multiplied by its distance from the new, total CE. Therefore:

100 D = 101 (6.9 - D) and
201 D = 696.9 and D = 3.47 feet, as shown on the drawing.

The lead of a sailing multihull is an entirely different matter and is often close to zero. The water forces against the hulls are variable, depending on whether the windward hull is partially in the water or completely exposed. When the windward hull is out of the water, the resultant sail force is well to windward of the single or combined lateral plane area of the hulls. This results in a turning moment that turns the boat to leeward (lee helm), which is prevalent in some multihulls. See Sail Area in *Chapter Ten*.

The center of lateral plane (CLP) is the center of the profile area of the under-water portion of the hull and keel but not including the rudder. This is the shaded area of Figure 16-3. The area and center of area may be calculated as in Figure 9-1, using Simpson's First Rule. Here, the depth of the profile is measured down from the waterline and used with Simpson's Numbers. The CLP is calculated by extending the table of areas. In the same manner as the CB was found in the displacement calculations of *Chapter Nine*.

The lateral plane center may also be found by tracing the underwater profile on a piece of cardboard and carefully cutting away the excess. This includes the keel but not the rudder. The cardboard is then balanced on a straightedge or on the point of a pin to find the CLP. (Shaded Figure 15-3) If the separation of the CLP and the CE is not adequate, the sail plan is re-drawn or the keel is moved or a long keel may be re-shaped. Any keel and ballast movement will change the LCG and the weight calculations of *Chapter Eight* will have to be updated. This constant checking and re-checking is a necessary part of boat design. The designer must always remember a slight alteration may change other important factors. It must be strongly noted, the preliminary sail plan and underwater profile are drawn before the hull lines are started.

Part II MASTS

FREE STANDING MASTS
(Without rigging)

Masts that are not supported by wire rigging, by preference, are used on a few sailboats and are usually heavier than masts with rigging. The load is entirely in bending and the mast acts like a cantilever beam. The loading may be calculated by multiplying the total sail area by the pounds per square foot (kg/m^2) of wind force. The wind force may be estimated from the formula: (Velocity Pressure of Air)

P (psf) = .004 V^2 (kt) and P (kg/m^2) = .00565 V^2 (km/hr)

For example, if the wind is at 20 knots, the velocity pressure in pounds per square foot is equal to .004 V^2. This is .004 multiplied by 400 which equals 1.6 pounds per square foot. Refer to the table in the following text on masts with rigging.

We assume the wind force to be uniformly distributed over the height of the sail even though the sail is usually triangular with a pointed top and the wind speed varies with the height above the water. The wind speed at the top of a mast may be twice that at deck level as the friction with the water surface slows the air mass moving over it.

The bending moment (BM) of a uniformly loaded cantilever beam is BM = WL / 2, where W is the total load and L is the mast length. We want the mast to stand in hurricane force winds and we use 80 knots (148.3 km/hr) in the calculation for wind force. The required section modulus of the mast is the bending moment divided by the bending stress allowed for the material. SM = BM / S. If the mast is a built up structure instead of a simple round or square tube, the combined section modulus of the structure must be carefully obtained.

For example, if we have 800 sqft (74 sqm) on a 50 ft (600 in) (15.25 m) mast length to the deck, the wind force is .004 (80^2) = 25.6 psf (124.3 kg/m^2) and the total load is 20480 pounds (9300 kg). Assume we use a glass fiber mast with 90 percent of the fibers uni-directional, resulting in a bending strength (from laboratory testing) of 50,000 psi (344,750 kPa) 3518 kg/cm^2. The required section modulus is WL / 2S and:

SM = 20480 lb (600 in) / 2 (50,000 psi) = 122.88 in³
SM = 9300 kg (15.25 m) 100 / 2 (3518 kg/cm²) = 2016 cm³

If the chosen mast section is to be a hollow circle, the section modulus is SM = pi (od⁴-id⁴) / 32 od, using the outside and inside diameters. After making two or three trial calculations, we find a section of 15 inch outside diameter (38 cm) and 13.25 in (33.7 cm) inside diameter has a section modulus of 129 in³ (2124 cm³) and is satisfactory. The section modulus of other shapes can be found in an engineering handbook.

In conclusion, it must be again emphasized all free standing masts must be set on the keel and there is a large side load at the deck or cabin top. There must be extra deck beams and carlins to resist this side load, spaced not more than 12 inches (30.5 cm) apart and epoxy glued or continuously welded. These extra deck beams should be placed over an area at least 5 feet (1.5 m) in length.

MASTS WITH RIGGING

As the wind force hits the sails, the mast tends to bend to leeward but is kept in a straight line by the windward shrouds and the windward spreaders. The load thus produced in the rigging pulls down on the mast and puts the mast in compression. We must calculate this compression load and use Euhler's long column formula to calculate the required moment of inertia of the mast section.

Three commonly used methods of calculating sailboat mast compression loads have been in existence for many years and have been noted in the excellent reference, *Skene's Elements of Yacht Design*, (1948 & 1973, Dodd, Mead & Co.) These methods will be explored and examples given.

The velocity pressure of air may be found in an engineering handbook, as previously noted and may be expressed as P (psf) = .004 V2 (kt). Larger hulls carry full sail in stronger winds than smaller boats. In our calculations, we must use an appropriate wind force for certain waterline lengths, as follows:

Waterline length	Wind velocity	Wind Pressure
25 ft & shorter	20 kt	1.6 lbs/sqft.
30	24	2.3
35	27	2.9
40 ft. & longer	30 kt	3.6 lbs/ sqft.
7.6 m & shorter	37 km/hr	16.2 kg/cm2

Waterline length	Wind velocity	Wind Pressure (Cont.)
9.15 m	44.5	23.3
10.7 m	50	29.4
12.2 m & longer	55.6 km/hr	36.5 kg/cm²

MAST PANEL COMPRESSION

The length of the mast above deck is divided into panels between the spreaders, from the lower spreader to the deck and from the upper spreader to the masthead. A uniformly distributed wind load is calculated from the mainsail area multiplied by the wind pressure from the above table. Interpolation may be made for different waterline lengths.

For example, we assume a 28.3 ft (8.6 m) waterline length sloop with a 280 sqft. (26.0 sqm) mainsail and a 346 sqft. (32.1 sqm) fore triangle. The mast is 46 ft (14 m) above deck, with 24 ft (7.3 m) to the lower spreader. The total wind load is 280 sqft. times 2.0 lbs/sq.ft, divided by the length of the mast (46ft). This is 12.2 lbs/ft which is multiplied by the panel length and half of the load is applied at each end of the panel. Thus, the upper panel has a load of 12.2 x 22ft / 2 = 134 at the masthead and at the upper spreader. The masthead also has the load of the fore tri-angle where the jibstay is attached. We use the fore triangle area at the masthead. The load at the spreader and the deck is then used with the spreader length (deck width) in a ratio to determine the compression load in each panel. That is, load divided by spreader length equals panel compression divided by the panel length. For the upper panel; (760 / 3) x 22 ft = 5573. For the lower panel; 906 x 24 / 3.5 = 6213 pounds. We add the two panel loads and multiply by 110% to get the total mast compression load. (12,965 lbs) (5886 kg) The additional ten percent allows for the weight of the mast, sails, boom and rigging and the pull of the halyards.

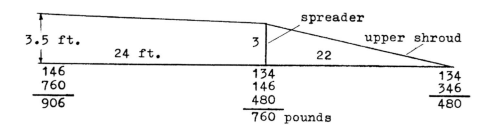

For preliminary estimates, the mast compression may be calculated by the formula:

Compression = 0.75 x Total Sail Area x Waterline Length. In the above example, C = .75 x 626 x 28.3 = 13,287 pounds. In SI units, Compression (kg) = 12.1 (sail area (m²) x waterline length (m)). C = 12.1 x 58.16 x 8.6 = 6052 kg.

<u>Mast compression</u> loading may also be found by drawing a force polygon, as in Figure 15-4. Using the previous example, the total wind force is represented in an athwartships direction by the mainsail area multiplied by 2.0 lbs/sqft (280 x 2 = 560 lb) (254 kg). This load is taken half at the masthead and half at the spreader. Using an exact scale drawing of the athwartships rigging and mast, each area around the rigging is denoted by a letter (Bow's Notation). The upper mast panel is noted as BF, the upper part of the upper shroud is AF, the spreader is FE and the lower shroud is DE.

The force polygon is started by drawing, to an exact scale, the wind force at the masthead, AB and the wind force at the spreader, BC, in a horizontal direction. The compression in the mast panels is vertical and vertical lines are drawn from B and C. Lines exactly parallel to the upper and lower portions of the upper shroud are drawn from point A. The upper portion intersects the vertical from B at point F, which is one end of the spreader. A line parallel to the spreader gives the intersection E, which is the other end of the spreader. A line parallel to the lower shroud from point E intersects the vertical from C at point D. This gives line CD which is the compression in the lower panel of the mast.

The load in each member of the force polygon may then be scaled. The compression in the lower panel of the mast is represented by CD and is scaled at 4330 pounds. The upper panel compression is 1930 pounds. These two results are added and doubled to account for the additional loads of the jibstay, backstay, pull of the halyards and weight of the mast, sails and boom. Thus we have a total compression load of 6260 x 2 = 12,520 pounds (5684 kg), by this graphical method of solution.

<u>The righting moment method</u> is commonly used for determination of the mast compression load as the hull righting moment equals the wind heeling moment at any particular angle of heel. This method works well for average sailboats but it does not take into account a hull with a very small or large, sail plan.

The righting moment at thirty degrees of heel is taken from the stability calculations of *Chapter Ten*. If the righting moment is not available for an existing hull, it may be estimated from the formula for ballasted sailboats only:

RM (ft-lb) = .03 (LWL)^{4}ft (At thirty degrees of heel)
RM (kg-m) = 0.5 (LWL)^4 m.

For example, if a ballasted sailboat has a thirty foot waterline length, the fourth power of thirty is 810,100. The estimated righting moment at thirty degrees of heel is .03 multiplied by 810,000. This is 24,300 foot-pounds.

This righting moment is divided by the half beam at the mast and multiplied by three to account for the higher righting moments at higher angles of heel. Using the hull in the previous examples, the righting moment is 21,000 ft-lbs (2908 kg-m) and the half beam is 4.5 ft (1.37 m). The calculated mast compression is then 21,000 x 3 / 4.5 = 14,000 pounds (6356 kg).

MAST SIZE

The dimensions and wall thickness of a sailboat mast are obtained from the moments of inertia in both the fore and aft ($I_{l\ in}^4$) and athwartships (It in^4) directions. This method is for supported masts with shrouds. The mast compression load as found above is used in Euler's long column formula along with the elastic modulus (E) of the mast material. E may be taken as (psi) 1 x 10^6 for wood and 10 x 10^6 for aluminum, (.07 x 10^6 kg/cm^2 and .7 x 10^6 kg/cm^2) (pi^2 equals 9.87)

I = WL^2 / pi^2 x E (Either English or Metric units) where W is the compression load in pounds or kg and L is the length from deck to top of jibstay (inches or cm) for I_l and length from deck to top of lower shroud for It.

Since the spread of the lower shroud is not as great as the spread of the head-stay and backstay, a factor of safety of two is used in calculating It. Euler's formula also uses a factor for the rigidity of the ends of the column. If the mast is stepped on deck (two pinned ends), the factor is one. If the mast is stepped on the keel (one end fixed and one end pinned), the moment of inertia is divided by two.

For example, if the compression load is 14,000 lbs. (6356 kg) on an aluminum mast and the length to the jibstay is 46 ft x 12 = 552 inches (1402 cm), the length to the lower shroud is 24 ft x 12 = 288 inches (731.5 cm), the required moments of inertia are: (Stepped on keel)

I_L = 14000 (304704) / 9.87 (10 x 10^6) 2 = 21.6 in^4
I_t = 14000 (FS=2) (82944) / 9.87 (10 x 10^6) 2 = 11.8 in^4
I_L = 6356 (1965604) / 9.87 (.7 x 10^6) 2 = 904.1 cm^4
I_t = 6356 (535092) 2 / 9.87 (.7 x 10^6) 2 = 492.3 cm^4

The physical dimensions of the required mast may be found from manufacturer's catalogs or they may be calculated from the formula for hollow ellipses;

$I = (pi / 4) (a^2) (a + 3B) t$ (pi equals 3.1416) where t is the wall thickness, "a" is half the longitudinal (or athwartships) outside dimension and "B" is half the other outside dimension. Most masts approach the shape of an ellipse but other shapes must be calculated.

Using the previous example, we may find an available mast extrusion that is 8 inches by 5 inches by 0.2 inch wall thickness. The moments of inertia of this aluminum extrusion are $I_L = 28.8$ and $I_t = 14.2$ in^4. These values are greater than those required and the mast section is satisfactory, as shown by the previous formula:

$I_L = (pi / 4) (16) (4+7.5) .2 = 28.8$ in^4
$I_t = (pi / 4) (6.25) (2.5+12) .2 = 14.2$ in^4

RIGGING SIZES

On cruising sailboats it is customary to have all stainless steel wire rigging the same diameter. In this manner, all end fittings, clevises and turnbuckles are the same size. The wire size is determined from the load on the lower shroud.

The diagram in the section on mast panel compression shows the lower panel load as 6213 pounds (2821 kg) which is about the same as the lower shroud, in length. Ten percent is added as a factor of safety, making the lower shroud load 6834 pounds (3103 kg). A table of breaking strength of stainless steel wire rope shows the next largest diameter as one-quarter inch (6.35 mm).

The force polygon method of Figure 15-4 shows the lower shroud load of 2420 pounds which is multiplied by a factor of safety of 2.5, giving 6050 lbs (2747 kg).

The Righting moment method uses a lower shroud load of 0.5 of the compression load of 14,000 pounds (6356 kg). This gives a shroud load of 7000 pounds (3178 kg).

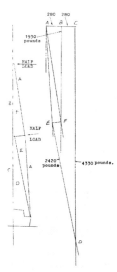

Figure 15-4

Force Polygon with athwartships mast loads contributing to mast compression. Sides of the polygon are exactly parallel to the rigging scale drawing. The compression load thus obtained is doubled to account for fore-aft loads of rigging, booms, sails and halyards.

SUMMARY

We cannot say one particular sailing rig is any better than another as each has its place in a particular area of sailing. Selecting a type of sail plan is like buying a suit of clothes. Everyone has their individual tastes. The question of having the headstay at the masthead or somewhat below is all a matter of owner preference.

New types of sails and equipment to set sails are being developed each year to make sail handling easier. Some owners prefer this while others like the physical exercise of changing sails and cranking winches. Some manufacturers try to copy the innovations used on racing sailboats, while others move in the opposite direction by using free standing masts without rigging on cruising sailboats.

This chapter has mentioned a few of these alternatives and the design methods used to engineer them. Light weight and simplicity are always enviable design objectives but attempts in this direction usually lead to higher costs for the owner.

CHAPTER SIXTEEN

BALLAST LOCATION & CONSTRUCTION

This chapter explains the location of the ballast and how it is attached to the hull on both powerboats and sailboats. The need for ballast to increase the range of stability was discussed in *Chapter Ten*.

Ballast may be inside or outside the hull and it usually consists of lead, except steel is used on steel hulls. The density of lead is 700 lb/cuft (11213 kg/m^3) and steel is 490 lb/cuft (7840 kg/m^3). Often, a combination of lead pellets and polyester resin is used in the keel cavities. When lead ballast is installed in an aluminum hull, either inside or outside, the aluminum must be insulated from the lead with a thick plastic sheet or neoprene rubber or thick epoxy resin, to prevent corrosion.

POWERBOATS

Ballast is not usually necessary on a modern, "V" bottom powerboat but it may be installed where there is a high center of gravity and the boat has a tendency to roll. An example of this is a large recreational powerboat that has a steel superstructure on a steel hull. Ballast can be added as shown in Figure 16-1, either with steel angles or a flat plate welded to the keel. Two to eight percent of displacement is normally sufficient ballast weight in powerboats for the problem of reduction in roll but heavier ballast may be required to increase the range of positive stability to a desirable seventy degrees of heel.

Any ballast added to the hull to achieve level trim must be secured to the frames, otherwise it may move to the low side when the boat heels. Ballast must not rest on the hull plating (shell) as the concentrated load may deform the hull. Frames must not be more than 12 in (30.5 cm) apart in the area of the ballast.

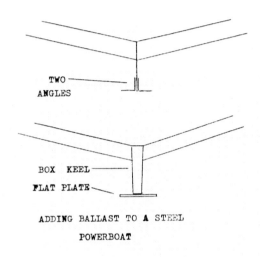

TWO ANGLES

BOX KEEL
FLAT PLATE

ADDING BALLAST TO A STEEL
POWERBOAT

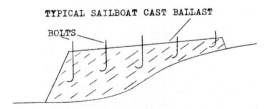

TYPICAL SAILBOAT CAST BALLAST

BOLTS

Figure 16-1

Various types of ballast.

SAILBOATS

Customary sailboat construction locates the ballast below and in contact with the keel with the outside shape conforming to the lines of the hull. Figure 16-1. The calculation of the height and length of this ballast is lengthy but usually determined on the second or third try. The ballast length is divided into an even number of equally spaced stations so Simpson's Rule may be used with the sectional areas to determine volume and center of gravity of the ballast. This is entered into the weight calculation of *Chapter Five* and the ballast shape is then revised until the ballast weight and total boat center of gravity is correct.

Another approach to sailboat ballast is the fin keel and torpedo shaped ballast as described in Figure 12-6. This has been used on racing sailboats such as the STAR class for over sixty years in an attempt to lower the center of gravity.

Some of the America's Cup sailboats have used short, almost horizontal wings extending outboard from the ballast at the bottom of a fin keel. This is an attempt to lower the center of gravity of the boat in another manner. When hauled out, the boat must be set on blocks carefully so these wings of lead are not damaged.

KEEL BOLTS

As shown in Figure 16-1, keel bolts of silicon bronze are normally cast into the ballast with the top ends threaded to take large washer plates and nuts inside the hull. There are two bolts through the floor timber at each frame. There should be a minimum of four keel bolts.

If the keel is not wide enough to have two bolts, side by side, the bolts will alternate on the port and starboard sides of the centerline. If the ballast tapers to a point at the forward end, there will be a through bolt about 12 inches (30.5 cm) from the end instead of having the bolt cast in place.

The size of the keel bolts is calculated by equating the moment produced by the weight of the ballast to the resisting moment of the bolts. For example, if the ballast weight is 10,000 lbs (4540 kg) and its CG is 10 inches (25.4 cm) below the top of the ballast and the distance from a keel bolt to the opposite side of the ballast is 5 inches (12.7 cm), the resulting load on the keel bolt is 10,000 (10) / 5 = 20,000 pounds (9080 kg). We use a yield strength of 20,000 psi - 137,800 kPa or 1406 kg/cm²- for either stainless or silicon bronze bolts. The required bolt area is then: 20,000 / 20,000 = 1 sqin (6.45 sqcm). The required diameter is 1.13 in (2.9 cm). If there are four bolts, the factor of safety is four. Factors of safety of ten are standard with ballast bolts.

Boatbuilders have many traditions and many have long used rules of thumb for the size of ballast bolts. One rule states the diameter of each bolt should not be less than the square root of: The ballast weight in tons divided by the number of bolts. Another rule has the total area of the keel bolts not less than the ballast weight in pounds divided by 1500. The total area of the bolts (not less than four) is in square inches.

It is not good practice to limit the number of keel bolts to reduce costs. The load of the ballast weight should be distributed over the length of the ballast with bolts at every hull frame. If the ballast length spans five frames, there should be ten keel bolts.

SUMMARY

This chapter has shown steel plate or angles installed on powerboats to lower the center of gravity and the location of ballast on sailboats. Keel bolts are used on sailboats to secure the ballast to the hull and their size and installation has been explained.

Ballast in any boat is another item that is difficult to change after the boat is completed. The calculations for weight and location must be exact. Unless changes have been made to the boat, the installation of trimming ballast shows poor workmanship and it takes away from valuable storage space inside the hull.

CHAPTER SEVENTEEN

DESIGN & CONSTRUCTION MISTAKES

Experience is the best teacher and everyone learns from accidents and mistakes that frequently occur throughout the boating industry. This chapter will briefly discuss some of those mistakes, hoping they will not be repeated.

THE WRONG ALLOY

A brass valve was installed in the sea water supply to an air conditioning condenser, on a glass fiber hull. No one was living on the boat and it sunk at the dock one night. When the boat was pumped dry, the brass valve was found to be completely disintegrated. Apparently, there was an excessive amount of zinc in the brass alloy and galvanic action with the monel tubing inside the condenser caused the zinc to be removed from the metal.

This is a case where the manufacturers' instructions were not followed and disaster resulted. A plastic ball valve is probably the best answer for this installation. Certainly, there should be a valve on all through hull fittings, not only for repair and replacement but in case a pipe or fitting fails inboard of the hull.

DECK TO HULL JOINT IN A GLASS FIBER HULL

Water leaks were constantly being found inside the hull. Inspection of the attachment of the deck to the hull showed no sealant between the two glass fiber laminates and hollow pop rivets were used to secure the deck to the hull every 16 inches (40.6 cm). The glass parts were not touching each other between rivets. Stainless bolts and nuts should have been installed every 6 to 9 inches (15.2 to 22.8 cm) and permanent seam compound must be used. This joint takes a beating whenever the hull pounds against a pier and it is good practice to reinforce the area with two alternating layers of mat and woven roving extending over 12 inches (30.5 cm).

TANKS LOCATED AFT

Water and fuel tanks in a powerboat were located just ahead of the transom and when they were full, the boat trimmed down by the stern and the exhaust outlets were under the water. Water filled the exhaust line to the muffler and this increased back pressure on the engine's exhaust valves which made the engines hard to start. In addition, it was disturbing to see the extreme change in trim from full to empty tanks.

All the tanks should be close to the middle of the boat so trim is not easily affected and the tendency to pitch is reduced.

DISTRIBUTION OF WEIGHTS

A boat was built with all the weights aft. This resulted in a very narrow waterline forward and a tendency to pitch into a seaway. The engine space and large galley were aft in the hull, just below a large deck house located all the way aft. The forward portion of the hull had staterooms and the forward deck area was clear. This arrangement dictated very wide waterlines aft to get the volume to support the heavy weights located aft. This resulted in increased resistance as well as an uncomfortable motion. It is better design practice to have the widest waterline beam about fifty to sixty percent of the waterline length aft of the stem. In this example, it would have been better to have the deck house in the middle of the hull, with a clear deck both forward and aft.

BEWARE OF HIGH WEIGHTS

There was excessive rolling of a large motor yacht, even in a small sea and a high center of gravity was suspected. On investigation, it was found the main deck contained heavy carbon dioxide cylinders for the installed fire extinguishers, a large, walk-in freezer and refrigerator, heavy refrigeration compressors and a large hot water heater. Clearly, these heavy weights raised the VCG and contributed to the discomfort of the passengers.

All of this equipment should have been located in the hull, just above the keel and one stateroom located on the main deck in their place. Ballast was added.

Careful attention should be given to the stability calculations of new motor yachts, especially with the tendency to locate tenders, a crane, masts and small automobiles on the bridge deck above the main deck.

CATAMARAN BEAM AND CLEARANCE

A catamaran was found to pound in a small head sea and the speed was noticeably reduced whenever waves would hit the wing structure between hulls. On inspection, it was found the bottom of the wing was only 20 inches (51 cm) above the water. This distance was obviously too small and should have been 0.1 of the overall length. In addition, there was a narrow "V" shaped projection on centerline within 12 inches (30.5 cm) of the water. No reason could be found for this center-line projection.

The deck house on this catamaran was quite small and it did not have room for storage of galley supplies. The ratio of length to beam was 3.5 : 1 rather than a desirable 2.0 : 1. It would have cost very little to increase the width of the wing structure.

SAILBOAT KEEL WIDTH

The owner of a sailboat felt it was slower than other boats of the same length. Also, it was slow to tack and there was more leeway than other boats. When the boat was hauled out of the water, it was obvious what caused the problems. The maximum width of the keel was 30 inches (76 cm) and was apparently used for a gigantic water tank!

A sailboat keel is always more effective both in boat speed and resistance to leeway if it is as thin as possible. It is seldom necessary for the ballast width to be more than 12 inches (30.5 cm).

UNDERWATER ENGINE EXHAUST

A large motor yacht had the engine amidships with underwater exhaust. It also had internal deck scupper pipes leading from just inside the sheer to slightly above the waterline. At slow speeds, the engine exhaust bubbled up and entered the lower end of the deck scuppers. It was very disturbing to the passengers to see smoke rising from the deck scuppers!

This unusual coincidence did not occur at high speeds and probably could only be prevented by leading the exhaust aft to the transom. A similar condition exists with the exhaust coming out of the side of the hull just above the waterline. The exhaust gasses are directed at the boat in the next docking space, with very unpleasant results.

EXHAUST FROM A V-DRIVE

A gasoline engine was mounted with a V-Drive and the exhaust came from the forward end of the engine, made a 180 degree turn in the iron pipe and ran aft to the transom. The pipe was wrapped with fireproof insulation but was within one inch (2.5 cm) of the row of spark plugs. Inspection of the running engine inside a dark enclosure revealed some of the spark plugs were arcing to the exhaust pipe. It is understandable the owner complained of poor engine performance. A new exhaust pipe was fitted, leading to one side of the engine.

HEADROOM AT STEPS

The problem of headroom over a ladder or steps continues despite a basic rule to follow. The headroom over each step must be 80 inches (2 m). If the headroom is less than this, the overhead deck or roof, must be cut back to the extreme edges of the area of the steps. Sometimes a box must be installed over this opening in the overhead to allow privacy on the upper deck or to allow a door to be locked.

A roof overhang over an exterior walkway may not provide sufficient headroom at steps in the walkway. A sloped deck may present the same problem and all passageways on the boat must be carefully checked.

VENTILATION AT THE HELM

A one piece, curved, plastic windshield was installed at an enclosed helm station. This acted like a greenhouse and it was unbearably hot at the helm. Two water trap ventilators were installed on the pilothouse roof that helped to relieve the heat.

The curved, plastic windshields look fine in respect to styling but there should be a flat section on centerline with strong frames and an opening window. Windshield wipers are a good safety feature and should be installed on all windshields. If DC electric motors are used for the wipers, they can be turned off for ten minutes of each fifteen minute period to minimize drain on the batteries, if necessary.

BOLT ALL HARDWARE

There have been many occurrences of deck hardware pulled loose from the deck when it was only fastened with screws or only with two bolts. All deck hardware should have four bolts through the deck and a backing plate of aluminum which is one-quarter inch (6 mm) in thickness and an area equal to the area of the deck hardware. Use caulking at the bolt holes. The use of two screws and two bolts on a four hole cleat is not acceptable.

Cleats have been pulled from a deck by dock lines or by a towing hawser. In one accident, a boat was being towed and a deck cleat pulled loose. The tension force in the line pulled that cleat through a window of the towing vessel.

OPENING PORTS IN THE HULL

A motor yacht had six opening ports in the hull side, about 24 inches (61 cm) above the waterline. It was careless to let these ports open when underway. The boat ran aground, heeling the hull to a point where water poured inside the ports. The hull filled with water and capsized. This resulted in a costly pumping operation and rebuilding of the interior. Ventilation should be provided by ducts to the main deck rather than openings in the side of the hull. When electric power is available, fans provide hot or cold air to all compartments.

FLEXIBLE DECKS

The pilot house deck on a glass fiber boat was of core construction without beams to support it. This upper deck was noticeably flexible under normal walking loads. Two posts were installed under this upper deck to the lounge and galley area below. Surprisingly, the deck was still too flexible and investigation showed the glass fiber main deck was flexing also. This example indicated any supporting posts must extend to the bottom of the hull with additional posts under the lower decks, directly in line with the upper posts. If the lower post does not land on a frame, additional frames must be installed to properly support the compression load. The hull plating should not be used as a support for any loads.

RUDDER SUPPORT

A powerboat had excessive water leaks at the stern and inspection showed the weight of the rudder was bearing on the stuffing box. This produced excessive loads on the packing and leaking resulted. The rudder post should be long enough to extend to the aft deck. In this manner, an emergency tiller can be fitted from the deck. A support collar must be secured to the rudder post between the stuffing box and the steering tiller arm. This collar rests on an aluminum, steel or glass fiber plate secured to the hull framing.

If an outboard rudder is installed aft of the transom, the weight is taken by two or more pintles, strongly secured to the transom. The tiller arm extends from the top of the outboard rudder through the transom. A slit in a rubber sheet prevents most of the water from entering through the transom.

PROPELLER NOISE

Both small boats and large ships have problems with excessive noise emanating from the propeller area. This results from each blade throwing water into the hull. This can usually be reduced by having the clearance between propeller tip and the hull greater than twenty percent of the propeller diameter. The problem is greater with displacement speed hulls where the hull profile is at a large angle of slope in the area of the propeller. Large tip clearance is desirable if it can be accomplished without increasing the hull draft.

The problem becomes more difficult on an existing hull were the tip clearance cannot be changed. Noise reduction is normally accomplished with a very dense material such as a sheet of lead. This is the material normally used on engineroom bulkheads so the staterooms will be quiet. But, we do not want excessive weight aft and the use of lead is limited to a thin sheet. Extra framing, spaced ten inches (25.4 cm), inside a flat, empty tank has been installed with some success in reducing propeller noise.

LONGITUDINAL STIFFENERS

A racing sailboat experienced cracking of the hull amidships while underway. The bow and stern lifted up as water entered the open hull and she sank. Tension is set into the headstay and backstay on a racing sailboat which pulls the ends of the boat upwards. The hull must have additional framing both forward and aft to resist these forces. At the same time, the weight of the ballast in the middle of the hull has a downward force and the bending of the hull must be resisted by longitudinal stiffeners. The deck and the hull form a hollow box girder which also resists twisting and bending but this girder must be reinforced with internal stiffening. This is why the spacing of framing is such an important part of the calculations for hull thickness and framing. See *Chapter Six*.

SUMMARY

This chapter listed some accidents that have shown various defects in design or construction. We all learn from accidents and mistakes and it is important to objectively analyze each one so we gain insight on how to avoid these problems in the future. We are again reminded of the philosopher who said, "Those who do not learn from the mistakes of history are doomed to repeat them".

CHAPTER EIGHTEEN

DESIGN CONSIDERATIONS

FLEXIBILITY

The designer is often asked why they did a certain detail in a certain manner. The answer is readily obvious to anyone who has had a custom design prepared for them. The designer does what the client demands. The designer cannot afford to turn down a client because of disagreement over a small feature. There is usually some way to provide for the client's desires in a safe and seaworthy manner.

People come to a designer to find a unique design to their specifications and every year we see boats with features that have not been used before. The designer gets many different requests. I designed a fully decked boat that was intended for only a few hours run. The interior was completely empty. One client paid me to design three boats which were never built. First, he changed his mind on the type of boat he wanted and then poor health did not allow construction of the accepted design. I designed the first manufactured, glass fiber, center cockpit, sailboat with a walk through passageway. (Mistress 39). A designer has to be prepared to meet any request.

COMPUTERS IN DESIGN

Computer programs are available for most boat design problems and the fees for these proprietary programs can extend into thousands of dollars for the most flexible and accurate. Each designer must decide which suits their needs. Certainly, the generation of smooth, fair curves is a prime necessity. Once the hull lines have been developed, the mechanical production of the calculations is an easy matter, whether manually or on a computer.

When drawing the outboard profile (styling drawing) or even a detailed mechanical part such as the rudder post and tiller arm, it is usually much faster to draw on paper rather than with a computer. I have seen professional industrial designers do sketches or partially completed drawings, on ten sheets of paper before a final draft is made for one project. This is done so designers have drawings to refer to as their thought processes develop on the road to a successful completion. This procedure takes more time on a computer as prints on paper must be made as each step of the drawing is developed. If drawings are to be given to a builder, the designer must have a 24 inch plotter to generate readable drawings.

The computer produces drawings that are very neatly done when compared with manual drawings and this makes a good impression on the client. Changes to the design are easily done by computer and the computer is certainly necessary when providing data to numerically controlled manufacturing equipment.

Although the computer industry is an ever changing business, it is safe to recommend the fastest, highest capacity computer you can afford. Graphics, of any type, consume hard drive space in large quantities and files of this size can only be processed by a very fast chip. Granted, any computer can process the information but with a slow processor, you can take the family on an island's vacation before the computer has finished its task.

DESIGN PROGRESSION

The chapters in this book are arranged in the sequence the designer follows with a new design. It must be remembered each step in the drawing process requires a complete review of all which has been previously done. Double checking all drawings is a constant necessity. A change in engine size changes the speed calculations, the weight list, trim, the propeller and shaft size and possibly the stability calculation. When an owner requires some major change in the design, the designer can expect many hours of revisions to the drawings and calculations.

New concepts in styling, above the waterline, always present a challenge to provide adequate headroom and necessary accommodations for the interior. Arranging new interiors can be as diverse as the imagination allows but the necessities cannot be forgotten. There must be a drawer for each person on board, both at the berth and in the head. Shelves for spare parts and cleaning gear are always needed and twelve inches of wardrobe width is minimum for each person. Of course, these requirements are for a cruising boat. A racing hull may be as bare as a skeleton.

Fifty years ago, the superstructure (deck house) of a boat was designed to use wood planking or plywood and round shapes could only be achieved by shaping a large piece of wood into a much smaller piece of styling. With the advent of glass fiber and plastic foam, any conceivable shape is possible. The progress of boat design has definitely been related to the available materials. We can only speculate in the developments of the next twenty years but it seems the demand for more accommodations and cargo space will continue. To meet this demand, the hull sides will probably flare outboard above the waterline so there is a wider deck and more interior space. The present safety requirements for passenger vessels will possibly become more prevalent in recreational boats, as most boat owners will want increased safety and reliability in both design and construction.

MULTIHULLS

Multihulls have already taken over the commercial passenger boat market and their number will probably increase. The wide deck space and resistance to rolling are the features that make them popular. Multihulls have sometimes been limited to commercial docks as many marinas do not have berths for a large beam boat. This will change as multihulls become more popular for both power and sail.

It has always been a design headache to keep the hulls as thin as possible for minimum resistance but at the same time wide enough for comfortable accommodations. In all but the smallest catamarans, the galley and lounge are placed on deck and the hulls are used for inboard engines, tanks and berths. New designs will probably have the hull sides flare out above the waterline so wider berths can be installed.

SOME EXCEPTIONS

This book has investigated powerboats and sailboats intended for cruising and does not mean to ignore other hulls that are well intentioned. Open boats used for day sailing or powerboating are more numerous than any other type. They are designed with the same principles explained in this book. Racing hulls are necessarily light in weight, with few accommodations. They show the same design basics, refined to suit their purpose.

DEFT DESIGN

The designer is often asked, what is the most important aspect of hull design? Or, what do you look for in assessing a boat? The answer is, one factor is not any more important than another. Each chapter in this book concerns an essential point of design. All the design factors must be developed together to form a successful boat.

Naturally, safety is important and the designer would do well to keep in mind four points of construction besides the usual design considerations. They are abbreviated D.E.F.T. and are most often found to be less than adequate in existing hulls.

D - The attachment of the <u>Deck</u> to the hull in a glass fiber boat must be strong and watertight. A good sealing compound and bolts spaced every 6 to 9 inches, are necessary, whatever the configuration.

E - The <u>Engine</u> compartment must be watertight to the rest of the hull. Water leaks at hoses and fittings have often led to sinking.

F - <u>Framing</u> in every hull and deck is often omitted in glass fiber hulls. This has led to cracks in the laminate of deck and hull from excessive flexing.

T - Groundings and collisions usually occur at the bow and a water<u>Tight</u> compartment greatly reduces the chance of water migration. Usually this can be installed under the forward berth or under the anchor locker. Glass fiber hulls have overlay to the hull side to be watertight. Wood hulls use a partial bulkhead and watertight top. The interior of the compartment should be coated with epoxy resin.

Each designer will develop their own check list of important points they want to highlight in each design. This list grows with experience and with the accumulated information from the news sources. Smooth sailing is always the objective.

LIST OF ABBREVIATIONS

CE - Center of Effort of the combined sail area. The geometric center of the sail plan.

CLP - Center of Lateral Plane of the underwater profile of the hull. The geometric center of the hull profile including the keel but not the rudder.

cm - Centimeter. There are 2.54 centimeters in one inch.

Cp - Prismatic Coefficient or hull fineness coefficient.

/ - A slant is used to indicate "divided by" .This slant separates the numerator and denominator in a formula. In text the / refers to "per" as in LB/FT (pounds per foot.).

E - Elastic Modulus. A reference to the elasticity of a material, used in certain formulas.

FS - Factor of Safety.

ft - Feet of 12 inches. Ft multiplied by ft equals square feet (ft^2).

g - The acceleration of a body due to the force of gravity. Equal to 32.2 ft per $second^2$.

GZ - Righting Arm. The length of the lever arm used to right the boat to an upright position after it has been heeled by the forces of wind and water.

HP - Horsepower of an engine advertised by the manufacturer.

I - Moment of inertia ($inches^4$). Indicates the resistance to motion (stiffness) of a particular structural shape.

in - Inches

kg - Kilogram, equal to 2.2 pounds.

Km - One thousand meters in a Kilometer. The metric measurement of speed is kilometers per hour (Km/hr).

Kt - A knot or one nautical mile per hour of speed.

L - Length between stiffeners or supports in a hull.

lb - A pound of weight or pressure.

LCB - Longitudinal Center of Buoyancy. The geometric center of the under-water hull volume.

LCG - Longitudinal Center of Gravity. The total center location of all weights in a hull. The LCG and the LCB must be at the same location to keep the hull level.

M - Or "m" .One meter, equal to 3.28 feet.

mm - A millimeter. One thousandth of a meter.

N - Newton. A measurement of force in the metric system.

P - Pressure applied, usually in pounds per square inch (psi).

Pa - Pascal. A unit of pressure (stress) in metric terms.

pi - Pronounced "pie" .A mathematical constant equal to 3.1416. The circumference of a circle is equal to pi multiplied by the diameter of the circle.

psi - Pounds per square inch. A unit of pressure is sometimes represented by pounds per square foot (psf). One psi equals 144 psf.

RM - Righting Moment. The energy a hull provides to resist a heeling moment of wind or water.

RPM - Revolutions Per Minute of a rotating shaft.

S - Allowable stress for a particular material.

SM - Section Modulus. (inches^3) A measure of stiffness of a particular shape. Used in some formulas in place of I (see above), Moment of Inertia.

t - Thickness of a hull or deck or tank.

V - Velocity or speed of a hull.

 X - A symbol meaning multiplied by.

LIST OF PHOTOGRAPHS & FIGURES

6-9 - Wood hull bottom framing

6-10 - Ferro-cement hull bottom framing

6-11 - Quarter Sawn Lumber

7-1 - Calculations for full flotation

8-1 - Boat speed table

8-2 - Minimum propeller diameter table

8-3 - Propeller pitch table

8-4 - Propeller diameter table

8-5 - Propeller shaft diameter table

9-1 - Calculations for displacement and center of buoyancy

9-2 - Preliminary hull lines

9-3 - Planing powerboat hull lines

9-4 - Semi-planing powerboat hull lines

9-5 - Displacement speed powerboat hull lines

9-6 - Sailboat hull lines, plan and profile

9-7 - Sailboat hull lines, sections

9-8 - Catamaran hull lines I

9-9 - Catamaran hull lines II

9-10 - Table of changes to hull lines

9-11 - Various catamaran hull sectional shapes

9-12 - Table of offsets

10-1 - Stability sections, forward

10-2 - Stability sections, aft

10-3 - Calculations for righting arm (GZ)

10-4 - Curve of righting arms and the Rahola Criterion

10-5 - Powerboat curves of righting arms

10-6 - Sailboat curves of righting arms

10-7 - Catamaran righting arm and maximum sail area

11-1 - Construction plan

11-2 - Construction profile, forward

11-3 - Construction profile, aft

11-4 - Construction section of a glass fiber hull

11-5 - Construction section of a metal hull

11-6 - Construction section of a wood hull

11-7 - Deck plan

12-1 - Catamaran hull connecting beams

12-2 - Trimaran connecting beams

APPENDIX ONE

SUPPLIERS & MANUFACTURERS

The following list of Suppliers and Manufacturers in no way constitutes a complete directory of all the fine manufacturers and suppliers available throughout the country. This list does not recommend these companies, it should be used only as a reference. As always ask your friends for their recommendations. In most cases you will not be disappointed following their guidance.

SUPPLIERS

Boater's World: Boat Supplies 1-800-826-2628, 6711 Ritz Way, Beltsville, MD 20705

Boat/US: Boat Supplies 1-800-937-2628 880 S Pickett St. Alexandria, VA 22304

Defender: Boat Supplies 1-800-628-8225 P. O. Box 820 New Rochelle, NY 10802-0820

E & B Discount Marine: Boat Supplies 1-800-538-0775 P O Box 50050 Watsonville, CA 95077-5050

Home Depot: Tools/Supplies Located in most cities throughout the country. Look for them in your local phone books.

Jamestown Distributors: Boat Building/Repairing Supplies 1-800-423-0030 28 Narragansett Ave. P O Box 348 Jamestown, RI 02835

West Marine: Boat Supplies 1-800-538-0775 P O Box 50050 Watsonville, CA 95077-5050

MANUFACTURERS

Ameron Protective Coatings: Coatings, 800-926-3766, 201 North Berry Street, Brea, CA 92621

Apollo Diesel Generators: Gensets, 714-650-2519, 833 West 17th Street #3, Costa Mesa, CA 92627

Balmar: Alternators and Controls, 902 NW Ballard Way, Seattle, WA 98107

Caterpillar Inc: Engines, 800-321-7332, P O Box 610, Mossville, IL 61552

Cummings Southeastern Power Inc.: Engines, 305-821-4200, 9900 NW 77th Court, Hialh Gardens, FL 33016

Datamarine International Inc.: Electronics Instruments, 508-563-7151, 53 Portside Drive, Pocasset, MA 02559

Davis Instruments: Navigation instruments, 415-732-9229, 3465 Diablo Ave., Hayward, CA 94545

Detroit Diesel: Engines, 313-592-5000, 7215 South 228th Street, Kent, WA 98032

Espar Heater Systems: Cabin Heaters, 416-670-0960, 6435 Kestrel Road, Mississauga, Ontario, Canada L5T 128

Fireboy Halon Systems Division-Convenience Marine Products, Inc.: Fire suppression equipment, 616-454-8337, P O Box 152, Grand Rapids, MI 49501

Furuno USA Inc.: Electronics, 415-873-4421, P O Box 2343, South San Francisco, CA 94083

Galley Maid Marine Products, Inc.: Galley, Water supply and waste, 407-848-8696, 4348 Westroads Drive, West Palm Beach, FL 33407

Heart Interface Corp.: Inverters, Chargers, Monitors, Electrical 1-800-446-6180, 21440 68th Ave. South, Kent, WA 98032

Hubbell Wiring Device Division, Hubbell Inc.: Electrical products, 203-337-3348, P O Box 3999, Bridgeport, CT 06605

Icom America, Inc.: Electronics, 206-454-8155, 2380 - 116th Ave. NE, Bellevue, WA 98004

Indian River Battery: Rebuilt starters, alternators, motors, batteries, 561-562-3255, 3638 US Hwy 1, Vero Beach, FL

Interlux Paints: Varnish, Paint, Coatings, 908-964-2285, 2270 Morris Ave., Union, NJ 07083

Kilo Pak: Gensets, 800-824-8256, 190 S Bryan Road, Dania, FL 33004

Kop Coat Marine Coatings: Coatings, 800-221-4466, 36 Pine Street, Rockaway, NJ 07866

Marinco Electrical Products: Electrical products, 415-883-3347, One Digital Drive,

Novato, CA 94949

Mercruiser: Engines, Drives, 800-624-2499, P. O. Box 1226, Waterloo, Iowa 50704

Micrologic: Electronics, 818-998-1216, 20801 Dearborn Street, Chatsworth, CA 91311

Nautical Paint Industries: Coatings, 800-432-4333, 1999 Elizabeth Street, North Brunswick, NJ 08902

New England Ropes, Inc.: All types of line, 508-999-2351, Popes Island, New Bedford, MA 02740

Northern Lights: Gensets, P O Box 70543, Seattle, WA 98107

Onan: Gensets, 612-574-5000, 1400 73rd Ave. NE, Minneapolis, MN 55432

Paneltronics: Electrical panels, 305-823-9777, 11960 NW 80th CT, Hialeah Gardens, FL 33016

Perkins Power Corp.: 305-592-9745, 5820 NW 84th Ave., Miami, FL 33166

Powerline: Alternators and controls, 1-800-443-9394, 4616 Fairlane Ave, Ft Worth, TX 76119

Racor Division-Parker Hannifin Corporation: Fuel filters, 800-344-3286, P O Box 3208, Modesto, CA 95353

Raritan Engineering Company, Inc.: Heads, Treatment systems, Charging systems, 609-825-4900

Ray Jefferson Company: Electronics, 215-487-2800, Main & Cotton Sts., Philadelphia, PA 19127

Raytheon Marine Company: Electronics, 603-881-5200, 46 River Road, Hudson, NH 03051

Resolution Mapping: Electronic charts and software 617-860-0430, 35 Hartwell Ave. Lexington, MA 02173

Sea Recovery Corporation: Water purification, 213-327-4000, P O Box 2560, Gardena, CA 90247

Seagull Water Purification Systems: Water purification, 203-384-9335, P O Box 271, Trumbull, CT 06611

Starbrite: Coatings /Sealants 1-305-587-6280, 4041 S W 47th Ave Ft. Lauderdale, FL 33314

Statpower Technologies Corp: Chargers, Inverters, 7725 Lougheed Hwy, Burnby, BC Canada V5A 4V8

Teak Deck Systems: Teak deck caulking 813-377-4100, 6050 Palmer Blvd. Sarasota, FL 34232

The Guest Company, Inc.: Electrical components, Chargers, Inverters,

203-238-0550, P O Box 2059 Station A, Meriden, CT 06450

Trace Engineering: Chargers, Inverters, 206-435-8826, 5917 - 195th NE, Arlington, WA 98223

US Paint: Coatings, 314-621-0525, 831 South 21st Street, Saint Louis, MO   63103

Valspar: Coatings, 612-332-7371, 1101 3rd Street S., Minneapolis, MN   55415

Vanner Weldon Inc. Inverters & Chargers 614-771-2718, 4282 Reynolds Dr. Hilliard, Ohio   43026-1297

Webasto Heater, Inc.: Cabin Heaters, 313-545-8770, 1458 East Lincoln, Madison Hts, MI 48071

Westerbeke: Gensets, 508-588-7700, Avon Industrial Park, Avon, MA   02322

West System Epoxy: Gougeon Brothers, Inc., 517-684-7286, P. O. Box 908, Bay City, MI 48707

Woolsey/Z-Spar: Paint, Varnish, Coatings, 800-221-4466, 36 Pine St., Rockaway, NJ   07866

Yanmar: Engines, 800-962-1984, 951 Corporate Grove Drive, Buffalo Grove, IL 60089

Please mention this book, when contacting the above companies.

APPENDIX TWO

REFERENCES

Any design process uses the accumulated information from many sources and I am indebted to those who have published before this book. Boating has made giant advancements in the past fifty years and every designer relies on the technical papers, books and magazines to remain informed of the latest developments. The following references are just a few of those invaluable sources.

The Aluminum Association, New York City, Engineering Data for Aluminum Structures, 1972.

Philip J. Danahy, *Adequate Strength for Small High Speed Vessels* SNAME *Marine Technology*, January 1968.

Gougeon Brothers, The Gougeon Brothers On Boat Construction, Bay City, Michigan, 1985 and 1979.

C.A. Marchaj, Aero - Hydrodynamics Of Sailing, Dodd, Mead Co., 1979.

Robert J. Scott, Fiberglass Boat Design and Construction, 1996 The Society of Naval Architects & Marine Engineers, Jersey City.

Norman Skene and Francis Kinney, Skene's Elements Of Yacht Design, Dodd, Mead Co. 1973.

William A. Henrickson and John S. Spencer, A Synthesis of Aluminum Crewboat Structural Design, SNAME Marine Technology, January 1982.

Marine Engineers' Handbook, Labberton & Marks, Mcgraw - Hill Books, New York.

INDEX

C

D

Hull lines - 14-17, 50, 97, 101, 111-136, 140
Hull thickness - 59-80, 150, 151, 171, 183, 213

K

Keel bolts - 76, 205, 206
Ketch - 189

M

Mast - 47, 52, 75-79, 94, 143, 163-171, 187-201
Mercury - 45, 46
Metric System - 15
Moderate Speed Hulls - 97-101, 112, 113, 121-123, 130
Mold - 22, 69, 70, 164
Mold loft - 15
Multihulls - 23, 99, 127, 145, 161, 193

P

Piping - 44, 53, 93, 147, 152, 181-186
Planimeter - 55, 115, 140
Planing powerboats - 98, 101, 107, 112-121, 130, 131
Plastic Composites - 69
Pounds per inch immersion - 57
Prismatic Coefficient - 111, 113, 114, 116, 136
Propeller - 97-110, 123, 127, 151, 174, 212, 216

R

Rahola Criterion - 141-147
Reduction Gear - 97, 99-106
Rigging - 52, 75, 94, 165, 190-200
Righting Arm (Gz) - 137, 140-147
Round bottom hulls - 112, 117
Rudder - 101, 123, 151, 159, 172-179, 194, 212

S

T

V

W

GLOSSARY

This glossary has been compiled by the staff of Bristol Fashion Publications with the help of many writers. It will give you some of the most common terms used in boating and on boats. It is not intended to cover the many thousands of words and terms contained in the language exclusive to boating. The longer you are around boats and boaters the more of this second language you will learn.

A

Accumulator tank-A tank used to add air pressure to the fresh water system thus reducing water pump run time.

Aft-Near the stern.

Amidships-Midway between the bow and stern.

Antifouling-Bottom paint used to prevent growth on the bottom of boats.

Arrangement Plan-The drawing that shows the berths, Galley and Head inside the hull.

Athwartships-Any line running at a right angle to the fore/aft centerline of the boat.

B

Backer plate-Metal plate used to increase the strength of a through bolt application, such as with the installation of a cleat.

Ballast-Weight added to improve sea handling abilities of the boat or to counter balance an unevenly loaded boat.

Beam-The width of the boat at it's widest point.

Bilge pump-Underwater water pump used to remove water from the bilge.

Bilge-The lowest point inside a boat.

Binnacle-A box or stand used to hold the compass.

Body Plan-The drawing showing the shape of the hull in an athwartships plane. Also called Sections.

Bolt-Any fastener with any head style and machine thread shank.

Boot stripe-Trim paint of a contrasting color located just above the bottom paint on the hull sides.

Breaker-Replaces a fuse to interrupt power on a given electrical circuit when that circuit becomes overloaded or shorted.

Bridge-The steering station of a boat.

Brightwork-Polished metal or varnished wood aboard a boat.

Bristol Fashion-The highest standard of condition any vessel can obtain and the highest state of crew seamanship. The publishing company which brought you this book.

Bulkhead-A wall running across (athwartships) the boat.

Butt connectors-A type of crimp connector used to join two wires end to end in a continuing run of the wire.

C

Canvas-A general term used to describe cloth material used for boat coverings of any type. A type of cloth material.

Carlin-A structural beam joining the inboard ends of deck beams that are cut short around a mast or hatch.

Cavitation-Reduced-propeller efficiency due to vapor pockets in areas of low pressure on the blades. Turbulence caused by prop rotation which reduces the efficiency of the prop.

Center of Effort- (CE) The geometric center of the total sail plan on a sailboat. Used to determine lee or weather helm.

Center of Lateral Plane-The geometric center of the (CLP) underwater profile on sailboats used with CE, above.

Centerboard-A hinged board or plate at the bottom of a sailboat of shallow draft. It reduces leeway under sail.

Chafing gear-Any material used to prevent the abrasion of another material.

Chain locker-A forward area of the vessel used for chain storage.

Chain-Equally sized inter-looping oblong rings commonly used for anchor rode.

Chine-The intersection of the hull side with the hull bottom, usually in a moderate speed to fast hull. Sailboats and displacement speed powerboats usually have a round bilge and do not have a chine. Also, the turn of the hull below the waterline on each side of the boat. A sailboat hull, displacement hull and semi-displacement hull all have a round chine. Planing hulls all have a hard (sharp corner) chine.

Chock-A metal fitting used in mooring or rigging to control the turn of the lines.

Cleat-A device used to secure a line aboard a vessel or on a dock.

Clevis-A "Y" shaped piece of sailboat hardware about two to four inches long that connects a wire rope rigging terminal to one end of a turnbuckle.

Coaming-A barrier around the cockpit of a vessel to prevent water from washing into the cockpit.

Cockpit-Usually refers to the steering area of a sailboat or the fishing area of a sport fishing boat. The sole of this area is always lower than the deck.

Companionway-An entrance into a boat or a stairway from one level of a boat's interior to another.

Construction Plan-A drawing showing all the parts that make up the hull structure. The plan and profile are drawn.

Cribbing-Large blocks of wood used to support the boat's hull during it's time on land.

Cutless Bearing-A trademark for a rubber tube that is sized to a propeller shaft and which fits inside the propeller shaft strut.

D

Davit-Generally used to describe a lifting device for a dinghy.

Deadrise-The angle that a hull bottom makes with the horizontal. Measured in the aft part of the hull but more commonly at the stern. If the stern is flat from port to starboard, it has zero deadrise.

Deck Plan-A drawing showing all the structure and hardware on the deck.

Deck Camber-An arbitrary curve that the deck has from port to starboard.

Delaminate-A term used to describe two or more layers of any adhered material that have separated from each other due to moisture or air pockets in the laminate.

Device-A term used in conjunction with electrical systems. Generally used to describe lights, switches receptacles, etc.

Dinghy-Small boat used as a tender to the mother ship.

Displacement Hull - A hull that has a wave crest at bow and stern and which settles in the wave trough in the middle. A boat supported by its own ability to float while underway.

Displacement-The amount of water, in weight, displaced by the boat when floating.

Dock-Any land based structure used for mooring a boat.

Down Flooding-When water enters an open hatch or ladder.

Draft-The distance from the waterline to the keel bottom. The amount of space (water) a boat needs between its waterline and the bottom of the body of water. When a boat's draft is greater than the water depth, you are aground.

Dry rot-This is not a true term as the decay of wood actually occurs in moist conditions.

F

Fairing compound-The material used to achieve the fairing process.

Fairing-The process of smoothing a portion of the boat so it will present a very even and smooth surface after the finish is applied.

Fairlead-A portion of rigging used to turn a line, cable or chain to increase the radius of the turn and thereby reduce friction.

Fall-The portion of a block and tackle system that moves up or down.

Fastening-Generally used to describe a means by which the planking is attached to the structure of the boat. Also used to describe screws, rivets, bolts, nails etc. (fastener)

Fiberglass-Cloth like material made from glass fibers and used with resin and hardener to increase the resin strength.

Filter-Any device used to filter impurities from any liquid or air.

Fin keel-A recent type of keel design. Resembles an up-side-down T when viewed from fore or aft.

Flame arrestor-A safety device placed on top of a gasoline carburetor to stop the flame flash of a backfiring engine.

Flat head-A screw head style which can be made flush with or recessed into the wood surface.

Float switch-An electrical switch commonly used to automatically control the on-off of a bilge pump. When this device is used, the pump is considered to be an automatic bilge pump.

Flying bridge-A steering station high above the deck level of the boat.

Fore-and-aft-A line running parallel to the keel. The keel runs fore-and-aft.

Fore-The front of a boat.

Forecastle-The area below decks in the forward most section of the boat. (pronunciation is often fo'c's'le)

Foredeck-The front deck of a boat.

Forward-Any position in front of amidships.

Freeboard-The distance on the hull from the waterline to the deck level.

Full keel-A long used keel design with heavy lead ballast and deep draft. This keel runs from the stem, to the stern at the rudder.

G

Galley-The kitchen of a boat.

Gelcoat - A hard, shiny, coat over a fiberglass laminate which keeps water from the structural laminate.

Gimbals-A method of supporting anything which must remain level regardless of the boat's attitude.

Grommet-A ring pressed into a piece of cloth through which a line can be run.

Gross tonnage-The total interior space of a boat.

Ground tackle-Refers to the anchor, chain, line and connections as one unit.

H

Hanging locker-A closet with a rod for hanging clothes.

Hatch-A opening with a lid which openings in an upward direction.

Hauling-Removing the boat from the water. The act of pulling on a line or rode is also called hauling.

Hawsehole-A hull opening for mooring lines or anchor rodes.

Hawsepipes-A pipe through the hull, for mooring or anchor rodes.

Head-The toilet on a boat. Also refers to the entire area of the bathroom on a boat.

Helm-The steering station and steering gear.

Holding tank-Used to hold waste for disposal ashore.

Hose-Any flexible tube capable of carrying a liquid.

Hull lines-The drawing of the hull shape in plan, profile and sections (body plan).

Hull-The structure of a vessel not including any component other than the shell.

I

Inboard Profile-A drawing of the centerline profile of a boat showing the interior arrangement on one side.

Inboard-Positioned towards the center of the boat. An engine mounted inside the boat.

K

Keel-A downward protrusion running fore and aft on the center line of any boat's bottom. It is the main structural member of a boat.

King plank-The plank on the center line of a wooden laid deck.

Knees-A structural member reinforcing and connecting two other structural members. Also, two or more vertical beams at the bow of a tugboat used to push barges.

L

Launch-To put a boat in the water.

Lazarette-A storage compartment in the stern of a boat.

Lead-The material used for ballast. Also, pronounced "leed", (as in leading a horse) when denoting the distance separating CE and CLP in a sail plan. (See above)

Limber holes-Holes in the bilge timbers of a boat to allow water to run to the lowest part of the bilge where it can be pumped out.

LOA-Length Over All. The over all length of a boat.

Locker-A storage area.

Log-A tube or cylinder through which a shaft or rudder stock runs from the inside of the boat to the outside of the boat. The log will have a packing gland (stuffing box) on the inside of the boat. Speed log is used to measure distance traveled. A book used to keep record of the events on board a boat.

LWL-Length On The Waterline. The length of a boat at the water line.

M

Manifold-A group of valves connected by piping to tanks. They allow filling and removal from one or more tanks.

Marine gear-The term used for a boat's transmission.

Mast-An upward pointing timber used as the sail's main support. Also used on power and sail boats to mount flags, antennas and lights.

Metacenter-A graphically determined point in stability calculations at one angle of heel.

Mile-A statute mile (land mile) is 5280 feet. A nautical mile (water mile) or knot is 6080.2 feet.

Mizzen mast-The aftermost mast on a sailboat.

Mold loft-A floor where hull lines are drawn full size. Patterns for construction are taken from the mold loft.

Moment of Inertia-Expressed as "I" in the units (inches^4). Indicates the resistance to motion (stiffness) of a particular structural shape.

Moment-A force (pounds) multiplied by the length of a lever arm (inches) to where the force is applied. (lb-in) If this is a rotating force on a shaft it is called torque or torsion. (lb-in). Bending Moment is the force applied to a plate or beam which tends to bend the beam or plate.

Moment of Inertia-Expressed as 'I' in the units (inches^4). Indicates the resistance to motion (stiffness) of a particular structural shape.

N

Nautical mile-A distance of 6080.2 feet

Navigation lights-Lights required to be in operation while underway at night. The lighting pattern varies with the type, size and use of the vessel.

Nut-A threaded six sided device used in conjunction with a bolt.

Nylon-A material used for lines when some give is desirable. Hard nylon is used for some plumbing and rigging fittings.

O

Outboard Profile-A drawing of the outside of a hull. Sometimes called a styling drawing.

Oval head-A screw head design used when the head can only be partially recessed. The raised (oval) portion of the head will remain above the surface.

Overhangs-The length from the bow or stern ending of the waterline to the forward or aft end of the hull.

P

Painter-A line used to tow or secure a small boat or dinghy.

Pan head-A screw head design with a flat surface, used when the head will remain completely above the surface.

Panel-A term used to describe the main electrical distribution point, usually containing the breakers or fuses.

Pier-Same general usage as a dock.

Pile-A concrete or wooden post driven or otherwise embedded into the water's bottom.

Piling-A multiple structure of piles.

Pipe-A rigid, thick walled tube.

Planing hull-A hull design, which under sufficient speed, will rise above it's dead in the water position and seem to ride on the water.

Planking-The covering members of a wooden structure.

Plug-A term used to describe a pipe, tubing or hose fitting. Describes any device used to stop water from entering the boat through the hull. A cylindrical piece of wood placed in a screw hole to "hide" the head of the screw.

Port-A land area for landing a boat. The left side of the boat when facing forward.

Prismatic Coefficient- (Cp) A dimensionless ratio of the hull displacement in cubic feet divided by the product of waterline length multiplied by area of the largest submerged hull section. (See text about Hull lines).

Propeller (Prop, Wheel, Screw)-Located at the end of the shaft. The prop must have at least two blades and propels the vessel through the water with a screwing motion.

R

Radar-A electronic instrument which can be used to "see" objects as "blips" on a display screen.

Rahola Criteria-Named after the person who proposed this measure of boat stability. Using a curve of Righting Arms at various angles of heel, the area under the curve to 40 degrees of heel must be 15 ft-degrees. (See text)

Rail-A non structural, safety member, on deck used as a banister to help prevent falling overboard.

Reduction gear-The gear inside the transmission housing that reduces the engine RPM to a propeller shaft RPM that is optimum for that particular hull and engine.

Ribs-Another term for frames. The planking is fastened to these structural members.

Rigging-Generally refers to any item placed on the boat after the delivery of the vessel from the manufacturer. Also refers to all the wire rope, line, blocks, falls and other hardware needed for sail control.

Righting Arm-A term used in stability calculations. The distance between the center of gravity of a hull and the center of buoyancy at one particular angle of heel.

Ring terminals-A crimp connector with a ring which can have a screw placed inside the ring for a secure connection.

Rode-Anchor line or chain.

Rope-Is a term which refers to cordage and this term is only used on land. When any piece of cordage is on board a boat it is referred to as line or one of it's more designating descriptions.

Round head-A screw or bolt head design with a round surface which remains completely above the material being fastened.

Rudder stock-Also known as rudder post. A piece of round, solid metal attached to the rudder at one end and the steering quadrant at the other.

Rudder-Located directly behind the prop and is used to control the steering of the boat.

S

Samson post-A large piece of material extending from the keel upward through the deck and is used to secure lines for mooring or anchoring.

Screw thread-A loosely spaced course thread used for wood and sheet metal screws.

Screw-A threaded fastener. A term for propeller.

Sea cock-A valve used to control the flow of water from the sea to the device it is supplying.

Section Modulus-Expressed as SM in the units (inches^3). Used in some formulas in place of "I", above. Indicates the resistance to motion (stiffness) of a structural shape.

Sections-Also, Body Plan. The shape of a hull in an athwartships plane, that is perpendicular to the waterline.

Shackle-A metal link with a pin to close the opening. Commonly used to secure the anchor to the rode.

Shaft-A solid metal cylinder which runs from the marine gear to the prop. The prop is mounted on the end of the shaft.

Shear pin-A small metal pin which is inserted through the shaft and the propeller on small boats. If the prop hits a hard object the shear pin will "shear" without causing severe damage to the shaft.

Sheaves-The rolling wheel in a pulley.

Sheet metal screw-Any fastener which has a fully threaded shank of wood screw threads.

Ship-Any seagoing vessel. To ship an item on a boat means to bring it aboard.

Shock cord-An elastic line used to dampen the shock stress of a load.

Slip-A docking space for a boat. A berth.

Sole-The cabin and cockpit floor.

Spade Rudder-A rudder that is not supported at its bottom.

Stability-The ability of a hull to return to level trim after being heeled by the forces of wind or water.

Stanchion-A metal post which holds the lifelines or railing along the deck's edge.

Starboard-The right side of the boat when facing forward.

Statute mile-A land mile which is 5280 feet.

Stem-The forward most structural member of the hull.

Step-The base of the mast where the mast is let into the keel or mounted on the keel in a plate assembly.

Stern-The back of the boat.

Strut-A metal supporting device for the shaft.

Stuffing box-The interior end of the log where packing is inserted to prevent water intrusion from the shaft or rudder stock.

Surveyor-A person who inspects the boat for integrity and safety.

Switch-Any device, except breakers, which interrupt the flow of electrical current to a usage device.

T

Table of Offsets-The collection of measurements taken from the Hull lines at each section (or station). Used to draw the hull lines full size on the mold loft floor. It shows the waterlines, butts, sheer, chine in width and height.

Tachometer-A instrument used to count the revolutions of anything turning, usually the engine, marine gear or shaft.

Tack rag-A rag with a sticky surface used to remove dust before applying a finish to any surface.

Tank-Any container of size that holds a liquid.

Tapered plug-A wooden dowel tapered to a blunt point and is inserted into a sea-cock or hole in the hull in an emergency.

Tender-A term used to describe a small boat (dinghy) used to travel between shore and the mother ship.

Terminal lugs-Car style, battery cable ends.

Through hull (Thru hull)-Any fitting between the sea and the boat which goes "through" the hull material.

Tinned wire-Stranded copper wire with a tin additive to prevent corrosion.

Topsides-Refers to being on deck. The part of the boat above the waterline.

Torque (Or Torsion)-The rotating force on a shaft. (lb-in)

Transmission-Refers to a marine or reduction gear.

Transom-The flat part of the stern.

Trim-The attitude with which the vessel floats or moves through the water.

Trip line-A small line made fast to the crown of the anchor. When weighing anchor this line is pulled to back the anchor out and thus release the anchor's hold in the bottom.

Tubing-A thin walled cylinder of metal or plastic, similar to pipe but having thinner walls.

Turn of the bilge-A term used to refer to the "corner" of the hull where the vertical hull sides meet the horizontal hull bottom.

Turnbuckles-In England they are called bottle screws. They secure the wire rope rigging to the hull and are used to adjust the tension in the wire rope.

V

Valves-Any device which controls the flow of a liquid.

Vessel-A boat or ship.

VHF radio-The electronic radio used for short range (10 to 20 mile maximum range) communications between shore and vessels and between vessels.

W

Wake-The movement of water as a result of a vessel's movement through the water.

Washer-A flat, round piece of metal with a hole in the center. A washer is used to increase the holding power of a bolt and nut by distributing the stress over a larger area.

Waste pump-Any device used to pump waste.

Water pump-Any device used to pump water.

Waterline-The line created at the intersection of the vessel's hull and the water's surface. A horizontal plane through a hull that defines the shape on the hull lines. The actual waterline or just waterline, is the height at which the boat floats. If weight is added to the boat, it floats at a deeper waterline.

Web Frame-The transverse structural members (frames) in a boat hull, installed port to starboard. Longitudinal frames are installed fore and aft.

Weight list-A compilation of every item in the boat. A calculation is made of the weight and center of gravity of everything on board. This is the only way a designer can estimate the displacement of the boat.

Wheel-Another term for prop or the steering wheel of the boat.

Whipping-Refers to any method used, except a knot, to prevent a line end from unraveling.

Winch-A device used to pull in or let out line or rode. It is used to decrease the physical exertion needed to do the same task by hand.

Windlass-A type of winch used strictly with anchor rode.

Woodscrew-A fastener with only two thirds of the shank threaded with a screw thread.

Y

Yacht-A term used to describe a pleasure boat of some size. Usually used to impress someone.

Yard-A place where boats are stored and repaired.

Books published by
Bristol Fashion Publications
Free catalog, phone 1-800-478-7147

Boat Repair Made Easy — Haul Out
Written By John P. Kaufman

Boat Repair Made Easy — Finishes
Written By John P. Kaufman

Boat Repair Made Easy — Systems
Written By John P. Kaufman

Boat Repair Made Easy — Engines
Written By John P. Kaufman

Standard Ship's Log
Designed By John P. Kaufman

Large Ship's Log
Designed By John P. Kaufman

Custom Ship's Log
Designed By John P. Kaufman

Designing Power & Sail
Written By Arthur Edmunds

Fiberglass Boat Survey
Written By Arthur Edmunds

Building A Fiberglass Boat
Written By Arthur Edmunds

Buying A Great Boat
Written By Arthur Edmunds

Outfitting & Organizing Your Boat For A Day, A Week or A Lifetime
Written By Michael L. Frankel

Boater's Book of Nautical Terms
Written By David S. Yetman

Modern Boatworks
Written By David S. Yetman

Practical Seamanship
Written By David S. Yetman

Captain Jack's Basic Navigation
Written By Jack I. Davis

Captain Jack's Celestial Navigation
Written By Jack I. Davis

Captain Jack's Complete Navigation
Written By Jack I. Davis

Southwinds Gourmet
Written By Susan Garrett Mason

The Cruising Sailor
Written By Tom Dove

Building A Fiberglass Boat
Written By Arthur Edmunds

Daddy & I Go Boating
Written By Ken Kreisler

My Grandpa Is A Tugboat Captain
Written By Ken Kreisler

Billy The Oysterman
Written By Ken Kreisler

Creating Comfort Afloat
Written By Janet Groene

Living Aboard
Written By Janet Groene

Simple Boat Projects
Written By Donald Boone

Racing The Ice To Cape Horn
Written By Frank Guernsey & Cy Zoerner

Boater's Checklist
Written By Clay Kelley

Florida Through The Islands
What Boaters Need To Know
Written By Captain Clay Kelley & Marybeth

Marine Weather Forecasting
Written By J. Frank Brumbaugh

Basic Boat Maintenance
Written By J. Frank Brumbaugh

Complete Guide To Gasoline Marine Engines
Written By John Fleming

Complete Guide To Outboard Engines
Written By John Fleming

Complete Guide To Diesel Marine Engines
Written By John Fleming

Trouble Shooting Gasoline Marine Engines
Written By John Fleming

Trailer Boats
Written By Alex Zidock

Skipper's Handbook
Written By Robert S. Grossman

Wake Up & Water Ski
Written By Kimberly P. Robinson

White Squall - The Last Voyage Of Albatross
Written By Richard E. Langford